R C Turner

ORCHIDS

Their Botany and Culture

Photograph by G.C.K. Dunsterville

Laelia purpurata

ORCHIDS

Their Botany and Culture

ALEX D. HAWKES

Foreword by John W. Blowers

Harper & Row, Publishers, New York and Evanston

This book is dedicated to my mother

KATHERINE HAWKES CHATHAM

with affectionate thanks for the orchids in my life

CONTENTS

FOREWORD

by John W. Blowers
Editor, *The Orchid Review*
Member, Royal Horticultural Society Orchid Committee

The old fallacy that orchids were only for aristocrats and millionaires has fortunately been exploded and thousands of present-day amateurs, many with moderate sized greenhouses, have found to their delight and enjoyment that most of the wonderful orchid plants may be grown and flowered with the same ease as other popular greenhouse plants.

But many of them, in beginning, are perhaps a little confused or bewildered by the infinite variety of orchidaceous plants, while veteran orchidists, discovering new species or varieties to add to their collections, are constantly seeking guidance about culture, identification or even pronunciation of the plants' names. Hybridists are seeking something different to augment existing variety or to extend the flower seasons in the greenhouse. Thus we have today an increasing multitude of orchidists, amateur and professional, interested in both the popular and the lesser known orchids, their progress or enthusiasm damped because of a lack of information about these plants.

The beginner, perhaps interested in the popular hybrids, seeks for a general comprehensive manual, up-to-date and comparable with those of the early days of orchid growing. No longer, however, need the orchidist, whatever his interests or abilities, indulge in lengthy, often fruitless searches through books and periodicals. A brilliant young orchidologist and author has come to their aid and further enjoyment in producing this book.

Born in Houlton, Maine, in 1927, the author, Alex D. Hawkes, started working with orchids at the age of 11 years in Orlando, Florida. At the age of 12 his first article on the subject was published, the forerunner of many brilliant papers on orchids and other tropical plants. As Editor of The Horticultural Publications, a group of five periodicals, including *The Orchid Journal* and *The Orchid Weekly*, he has written and published over 2,000 papers on these subjects.

This manual is not only the result of many years' conscientious study of the Orchidaceae, but has its backbone practical experience in the management of his own collection and the advantage of travelling to see and collect orchids in and from their native haunts. Throughout his travels in many parts of the world he has devoted himself assiduously to studying these habitats, recording his observations and conclusions in this volume, so that the reader may imitate these conditions and successfully cultivate and flower his plants.

Another important feature of this splendid book is the correctness of the nomenclature of the plants discussed. The author will be the first to admit that much remains to be corrected and put in order in the Orchid Family; but I know from his previous publications that where any confusion exists Dr. Hawkes is among the first attempting to unravel the errors and mysteries which unfortunately surround many orchidaceous plants. This manual is therefore one of the most up-to-date publications of its kind so far as correct nomenclature is concerned. The reader is not tongue-tied by pronunciation, nor need he any longer be embarrassed by orchid conversation when generic or specific names are included; the pronunciation is given for each genus and species included in the volume and is an important service of the work.

Orchids: Their Botany and Culture has everything—correct nomenclature, easy-to-follow pronunciation, photographs and drawings, details of numerous rare orchids, particulars of habitats, cultural instructions and gimmicks to increase the fascination of orchid growing for the beginner and to alleviate some of the long-standing problems for the professional and experienced orchidist. I have few doubts that this volume will remain a standard work for many years to come.

PREFACE

I have attempted to organize the present book in such a way that it will be useful to everyone interested in the subject—whether the reader be a veteran orchidist or a hobbyist who is trying his first specimens.

The work is divided into four principal sections. An introductory part, discussing orchids in general, takes up their basic botany, general appearance and variations, habits and habitats, economic importance, and gives a brief history of the early days of orchid cultivation.

Basic cultural requirements for orchids are considered next, with observations on the growing of orchids both indoors (as house plants) and outside, housing of the collection, propagation, potting, composts, seed-production and the rather specialized requirements of seedlings, and the treatment of newly-imported plants. A list of orchids especially recommended to beginners is provided.

A résumé of the entire orchid hybrid situation follows. One chapter is devoted to the mechanics of orchid breeding, and one to hybrids in general and their present numbers and status.

The largest part of the book discusses the kinds of orchids most common in our collections today. One hundred genera are included here. Hybridization, whether accomplished or prospective, is noted in detail, together with pertinent cultural notes for each genus. The major cultivated species (and variants) of the different genera are described, and in many cases illustrated. Flowering seasons are noted, also the geographical distribution.

The Appendix, with a brief introductory comment on names and classification, provides a complete phylogenetical list of the orchid family.

I would like to take this opportunity to express my gratitude to the following persons who have in many ways contributed to the making of this book:

Paul H. Allen and Dorothy O. Allen, Katherine Hawkes Chatham, Gordon W. Dillon, Harry A. Dunn, G. C. K. Dunsterville, Dr. Edward A. Flickinger, George Fuller, Miss M. Hawkes, the late Prof. Frederico Carlos Hoehne—Director of the Instituto de Botânica do São Paulo, Rodney Wilcox Jones, William Kirch—Orchids Ltd., Oscar M. Kirsch, Richard B. McAdoo, Lester McDonald, Rod McLellan Co., Mr. and Mrs. W. W. G. Moir, Fred A. Stewart—Orchids.

I

The Orchid Family

WHAT ARE ORCHIDS?

Orchids are flowering plants—as contrasted with such plants as mushrooms and mosses, which do not produce flowers. They are all members of a single botanical family, the Orchidaceae (the last five letters of which are pronounced like the three spoken letters, A-C-E).

Orchis maculata, a European representative of the genus on which the family Orchidaceae is based.

GEORGE FULLER

The orchid family belongs to the plant group called the monocotyledons, which are distinguished by having only a single seed-leaf upon germination. Plants that have a pair of seed-leaves at germination are known as dicotyledons. Although the irises, lilies, bromeliads, and aroids are also monocotyledons, the orchids—despite some occasional vague similarities—are only distant relatives. The closest allies of the orchids are the Apostasias (members of the family Apostasiaceae) and the Burmannias (family Burmanniaceae). Both groups consist of a few insignificant and seldom-seen terrestrial or saprophytic plants found mostly in tropical areas.

More than 24,000 different kinds of orchids grow wild throughout the world, and an even greater number of hybrids is now on register.

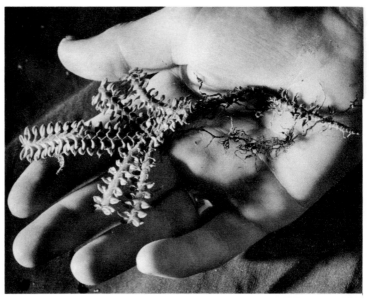

Dichaea muricata, one of the numerous and delightful "botanical" orchids. This example, a full-grown plant, was collected in southern Mexico (Chiapas).

Thus, in the Orchidaceae we have by far the largest assemblage of kinds of plants known in any flowering plant family—considerably more than 48,000 names being recognized.

Orchids are perennial herbs of varying growth habit—in the ground, on rocks, or perched on trees or shrubs. A few orchids grow in water, as semi-aquatics, and two extremely rare and unusual genera, the Australian *Cryptanthemis* and *Rhizanthella*, are subterranean, at most only the tiny flower-heads reaching the surface of the ground. The majority of orchids found in temperate climates are terrestrial in habit, while those from the tropics grow most frequently on trees or rocks.

FRED A. STEWART, INC.   WM. KIRCH—ORCHIDS, LTD.

Left, *Cattleya x Claire Ayau,* a fine contemporary hybrid of this popular genus. Right, *Dendrobium x Walter Carter*

WHERE ORCHIDS ARE FOUND

Generally, the layman believes that orchids are to be found only in the tropics, where they inhabit dank, steaming, excessively dark and "mysterious" spots in the jungle. This is almost completely incorrect. The Orchidaceae range to almost all parts of the globe, even to such illogical spots as the chill bleak meadows of Patagonia, the often frigid dales of Alaska, the snow-covered summits of the Himalayas, the parched sandy deserts of Australia and Africa, and—as semi-aquatic plants—the tannin-stained streams of our own Southeastern States.

The great island of New Guinea has more native orchids than any other place in the world, but it is closely followed in number of species by such areas as Colombia, Brazil, Costa Rica, Borneo, Java, and the Indian Himalayas. The State of Florida boasts almost ninety different kinds of indigenous orchids, and every state in the Union has at least a few orchidaceous representatives in its flora. Minnesota has officially adopted an orchid, *Cypripedium reginae*, as its state flower.

Certain areas that are presumed to possess extensive orchid floras have almost no native orchids or none at all. The Hawaiian Islands, for example, have only three small and insignificant native orchids. On the other hand, certain isolated insular groups, also in the Pacific, have relatively extensive orchid floras which are characterized by the dominance of endemism—that is, the plants are found only there and nowhere else in the world. This endemism is typical of the entire Orchidaceae, and considerable attention has been paid to it by students of the family and its distribution. Many members of the genus *Dendrochilum* (in particular of the section *Acoridium*) are known to exist only on special mountain peaks, or on a solitary peak, in the Philippine Islands and Borneo. Such examples of narrow endemism are legion in the orchid family, and form a subject for fascinating and instructive study.

COLORS, SIZES, AND FORMS

Orchid flowers are produced in all the colors of the rainbow. Green and brown, peculiarly enough, are probably the most frequent hues, as regards species producing them, despite the fact that an orchid is, to the layman, a lavender or magenta or "orchid" *Cattleya* or one of its allied groups. Colors such as white, yellow, blue, scarlet, orange, and virtually every other possible combination of every other hue are also known. Black orchids do not exist (true black as a color does not occur in flowers), but there are some species which bear blossoms whose parts are of such a dark, rich purple or maroon as to appear this shade. The best-known and most spectacular of these is the handsome Indonesian *Coelogyne pandurata*, though flowers with this exotic hue are also found in such genera as *Pleurothallis, Bulbophyllum, Maxillaria*, and a few others. True pink is perhaps the rarest color in the Orchidaceae, occurring only in a few Vandas and allied groups, and in the terrestrial groups *Satyrium, Disa*, etc.

In size, the flowers of orchidaceous plants exhibit a most remarkable range. Certain species of *Stelis, Taeniophyllum*, and *Bulbophyllum* possess the smallest of blossoms, these often measuring considerably less than 1/32″ in diameter when fully expanded. Conversely, certain species of *Sobralia* (notably *S. macrantha*) bear flowers upwards of one foot in diameter, and some of the fine contemporary "*Cattleya* group" hybrids reach almost comparable dimensions.

These flowers may be produced singly on more or less abbreviated peduncles (as, for example, all Maxillarias, Lycastes, Huntleyas, etc.), or in all possible combinations of quantity and arrangement up to several hundred per individual inflorescence (as in certain Epidendrums, Oncidiums, Dendrobiums, etc.)

A sizable volume could be devoted, without becoming unduly repetitious, to a discussion of the shapes of orchid blossoms. I shall at this time mention only the amazing examples of mimicry which we find in this family, such as the insect- or butterfly-like *Phalaenopsis* and *Oncidium Papilio* and *O. Kramerianum*, the reptilian appearance of most members of the section *Megaclinium* of the genus *Bulbophyllum*, the daisy-like inflorescences of many species of the section *Cirrhopetalum* of the same group, and the bee- or wasp-like similarity of many kinds of *Ophrys*. The imaginative observer can readily, with critical observation, also find such extraordinary similarities as the face of a tiny, leering elf in the column and lip of a *Dichaea*, a charming dancing doll in the blossom of an *Oncidium*, the gaping maw of a crocodile in the brown and purple sepals of a *Pleurothallis*, or a dove poised and ready for flight in *Peristeria elata*.

When taking up the forms exhibited vegetatively by orchidaceous plants, we are confronted by an extremely complex and diversified subject. This topic is discussed in the section of this volume devoted to the different kinds of orchids, hence we will not note it further at this time, except to mention that orchids are among the most incredibly varied of all plants in this respect, and here again innumerable pages of text and illustrative matter could well be devoted to a dissertation of even the most dominant variations.

HOW ORCHIDS GROW

In the warm regions of the earth, where orchids are the most numerous, they are for the most part air-plants, more correctly termed *epiphytes*. That is, they grow lodged on a tree or bush, but derive no nourishment from it. Many live equally well as *lithophytes* on barren rocks or cliffs, to which their fleshy roots cling with amazing tenacity.

FLORENCE B. JOHNSON

These dense colonies of *Laelia* (*Schomburgkia*) *tibicinis* are growing as epiphytes on a huge Ceiba tree in southern Mexico.

Many orchids grow wild on rocks along with other plants. These flowering specimens are *Angraecum giryamae*, in Kenya, East Africa.

This in itself is certainly evidence that they are not parasites (as many people believe), for bare stone offers very little in the way of food materials for any plant. They are both moistened and nourished in part by the rain, which carries dust and other minute particles whose minerals help to sustain them. The nightly dews also provide moisture. Any tiny bits of debris, such as falling leaves, dislodged bark or even dead insects which happen to fall about their roots likewise nourish the epiphytic orchids.

Some orchids, including almost all of those native to the temperate zones, grow in the ground, exactly as do "ordinary" plants, deriving their nourishment from the minerals and water found in the soil. These orchids are called *terrestrials*, to distinguish them from the tree-dwelling epiphytes or the rock-inhabiting lithophytes. Almost all terrestrial orchids can readily be identified as such by examination of their root-systems; in these ground-dwelling species the roots are usually furnished with a more or less prominent growth of threadlike root-hairs, which are normally absent in the epiphytic and lithophytic types.

The *saprophytes*, a third kind (or a fourth, if we count the litho-phytes as a separate category), live a peculiar sort of existence on dead and decaying animal or vegetable matter, usually in the ground or on rotting logs. These saprophytic orchids (which include only a few genera, notably *Corallorrhiza*, *Hexalectris*, and *Galeola*) are relatively little known, occur in all parts of the world but particularly in the tropics, and are virtually impossible to introduce into cultivation with any degree of success, because the delicate relationship between the roots of the orchid and its subsistence medium is seriously disturbed, if not destroyed, in transplanting.

H. E. ANTHONY   VEITCH

Left, a beautiful group of *Cattleya maxima* growing wild in a forest in Ecuador. Right, *Odontoglossum pendulum*

It is often difficult to classify orchids precisely as to growth methods since species (or genera) which may normally be epiphytes or lithophytes will possibly, through breaking of a branch or falling of a tree, be forced to take up life in the ground as terrestrial plants. Many orchids thus catapulted groundward develop a root-system almost precisely like that of the true terresterial members of the family, complete with intricate root-hairs. Many orchids (notably certain species of *Epidendrum, Oncidium,* and *Cymbidium*) do not exhibit any particular predilection for either an arboreal or terrestrial habitat, the same species occurring high in the trees above thriving specimens of the same kind in the soil below. This is also true of many erstwhile terrestrial orchids, which under favorable circumstances take to the trees, especially if a pocket of humus or detritus is present in a branch-crotch or comparable site.

Some orchids start out life as true terrestrials, growing in the ground in woods or thickets, then develop later into epiphytes. Among these are most species of *Pseuderia*, many Epidendrums and Renantheras, Vanillas, Galeolas, some kinds of *Arachnis* and *Vanda*, a few Dipodiums, and others. As the plants grow older and elongate, the basal

An unidentified species of *Microcoelia* found in Kenya, East Africa. This is one of the extraordinary totally leafless orchids.

FRANK PIERS

portion of the stem—that part which is in the ground—may completely deteriorate, so that the plant eventually lives attached only to the trunk of the tree or shrub on which it is growing.

Almost every possible intermediate condition of growth habitat is known within the many thousands of different kinds of orchidaceous plants.

The plants, as well, occur in all possible sizes. Certain Bulbophyllums and several species of the subtribe *Pleurothallidinae*, when fully mature, measure considerably under a quarter-inch in overall height. *Grammatophyllum speciosum*, the fabulous "Queen Orchid" of the Indonesian-New Guinean region, bears pseudobulbs often in excess of twenty-eight feet long, while several Dendrobiums have stemlike pseudobulbs only slightly less than twenty feet tall. Vinelike orchids,

GEORGE FULLER

This pot measures 2¼″ in diameter. The full-grown flowering orchid in it is *Pleurothallis microtatantha.*

A giant plant of *Calanthe veratrifolia* growing in the forests of Papua, New Guinea.

REVEREND N. E. G. CRUTTWELL

OCTÁVIO FONSECA

An immense plant of the spectacular *Brassavola Perrinii,* grown in its native Brazil.

Oncidium leucochilum as collected in southern Mexico (Chiapas). It is displayed by a Tehuana Indian from the Isthmus of Tehuántepec.

FLORENCE B. JOHNSON

such as *Vanilla, Galeola,* and *Vanda teres,* may attain gigantic lengths in the wild, upwards of one hundred feet, clambering over trees and undergrowth and forming virtually impenetrable masses of branching and rebranching stems. In the greenhouse, however, the grower need not fear that his plants will reach out of bounds.

THE ORCHID PLANT

The vegetative parts of orchid plants are almost as diverse in structure as are the flowers. Despite this, the various organs—roots, stems, leaves, and inflorescences—are confined to a comparatively few basic categories. The vegetative variations often form an important adjunct to the floral ones in the arrangement of the genera and species into a taxonomic system.

Classification by Style of Growth

One of the first readily usable systems of classification for the Orchidaceae was that proposed by Ernst Pfitzer in the late nineteenth century. Pfitzer's arrangement has formed the basis for most contemporary schedules, including that used in this work (see pages 262 to 272). His primary divisions were based on the vegetative structures of the plants. These were the *monopodials,* which are (in his translated words): "those which grow continuously in one direction only. Their stems lengthen indefinitely season after season, and bear aerial (adventitious) roots often along their whole length. The inflorescence is always lateral and is produced from the axils of the leaves or opposite to them."

Pfitzer's second vegetative division, which he called the *sympodials,* consists of "those in which the growth of the main axis, stem or pseudobulb soon ceases, usually at the end of one season's growth, and a lateral growth is produced in the following season." So far, he is referring only to vegetative growth. He then divides the sympodial orchids into two groups, based on flowering habits: those with a lateral inflorescence and those with a terminal (apical) one. A third category is also recognized—the *pseudomonopodials,* which are somewhat intermediate in vegetative structure between the monopodials and the sympodials. This small group is briefly discussed elsewhere in this chapter.

The monopodial orchids comprise only 2 subtribes, the *Sarcanthinae* and *Campylocentrinae,* out of the total of 88 now recognized in the orchid family. Examples are found in such genera as *Vanda, Aerides, Phalaenopsis, Renanthera, Angraecum,* and *Aerangis.* In these groups, as

DRAWING BY ALEX D. HAWKES

A species of *Brassia* showing the sympodial habit characteristic of a great many orchids.

in all other monopodial genera, the leaves are distichously arranged—that is, they are in two rows, one opposite the other, the leaves of one row alternating with those of the other. In some species (in *Phalaenopsis,* for example) the internodes are very short and the leaves hence become crowded; in other genera, the internodes are relatively distant from one another. The leaves are mostly longer than broad, and are variously notched or unequally 3-lobed at their apex. While the leaves are usually flat, or plane, some orchids (notably *Vanda teres* and all members of the genus *Luisia*) have leaves that are terete, much like the stems from which they arise.

In these monopodial orchids, the inflorescence is a raceme, or less frequently a modification of a raceme, such as a panicle. Very dense, many-flowered racemes occur in such genera as *Rhynchostylis, Aerides,* and *Sarcochilus*, while few-flowered ones are found in most of the commonly grown species of *Vanda, Arachnis, Trichoglottis*, and others. The most exuberant instances of branched panicles occur in well established specimens of such groups as *Aerides* and *Phalaenopsis*.

The pseudomonopodial orchids. Lying between the monopodial and the sympodial groups are the pseudomonopodial orchids, which are characterized by growth both in an apical direction season after season, and also in a horizontal or sympodial one. They form a minor aggregation which includes a few small American subtribes, containing such little-known genera as *Centropetalum, Pachyphyllum*, and *Dichaea*.

Thus, the vast majority of orchidaceous plants are characterized by a sympodial mode of growth. This includes all orchids possessing pseudobulbs and all whose stems mature (basically) within a single season's growth. A number of variations exist in this sympodial category, and some of these deserve attention.

In the sympodial orchids the new growth usually commences with the development of leaflike scales. Between the initial pair of scales and the true leaves that eventually arise, many intermediate forms are sometimes found. In pseudobulbous species with but few leaves, the pseudobulbs are often developed between the first pair of true leaves, and one or more leaves are additionally produced from the pseudobulb-apex as in *Odontoglossum, Oncidium*, and *Miltonia*.

In other species the vegetative axes are often prolonged into leafy stems of varying length and thickness. In both cases the old pseudobulbs and old stems persist for some time after they have become mature. The terminal pseudobulbs of the rhizome are usually the only flower-bearing ones, although in many species of such genera as *Epidendrum, Dendrobium, Pleurothallis*, and *Scaphyglottis*, blossoms are produced from the same pseudobulbs or stems for several successive years.

Many of the most handsome orchids in cultivation today are characterized by bearing their flowers in a lateral inflorescence. Among the more noteworthy of these may be noted such genera as *Dendrobium, Cymbidium, Oncidium, Odontoglossum, Maxillaria, Lycaste, Phaius, Stanhopea*, and *Bulbophyllum*, as well as a host of others. Variation in exact place of origin of these inflorescences is commonplace, some arising from the base or side of the pseudobulb, others on short leafless pseudobulb-like extensions produced near the bases of the true pseudobulbs, and yet others directly from the rhizome between the pseudobulbs.

Perhaps even more orchids (numerically) are typified by a terminal inflorescence. These include the ever-popular *Cattleya* (except for one or two species), all but two species of *Epidendrum, Laelia, Sobralia,* most of the immense subtribe *Pleurothallidinae,* and many others.

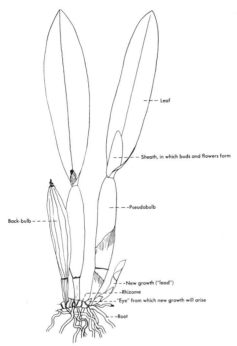

DRAWING BY ALEX D. HAWKES

The parts of a typical *Cattleya* orchid plant.

The Orchid Rhizome

A rhizome is found only in the sympodial types of orchid plants—except for a few in a drastically reduced state in the pseudomonopodials. The rhizome is actually a primary stem, from which arise the secondary stems. These may be elongated and leafy, relatively abbreviated and thickened into pseudobulbs of varying shapes and dimensions, or otherwise developed. The form of the rhizome itself varies from genus to genus, and often from species to species within a single aggregation. In many genera—most Masdevallias, many Dendrobiums and Oncidiums, for example—the rhizome is so shortened as to be scarcely apparent; because of this the plants assume a tufted or caespitose growth-habit. Most of the Cattleyas and Laelias, as well as many other orchids, have a more distinct rhizome that is prominently thickened. Conspicuously elongated rhizomes are found in such genera as *Bulbophyllum*, *Rodriguezia*, and *Coelogyne;* in such instances the pseudobulbs arise at varying distances from one another, thereby giving the plant a straggly appearance. Extremes of variation in rhizomes exist in

GEORGE FULLER

Masdevallia O'Brieniana, an example of sympodial growth in orchids.

virtually every orchid genus, and are too numerous to be mentioned individually here.

Orchid Roots

In the sympodial orchids the roots are normally produced from the rhizome. The roots of most orchids are cylindrical, often threadlike, either branching or not, and frequently long. In most members of the subtribe *Cypripedilinae*, and a great many other terrestrial species, they are furnished with numerous root-hairs.

The aerial roots of epiphytic (and lithophytic) orchids consist of a central axis, surrounded by a covering of loose, spongelike tissue, called the *velamen*, the cells of which when dry are filled with air only. This light covering, with its thin epidermis, absorbs moisture with great rapidity, and retains it for a considerable period of time. Generally the roots of epiphytic orchids are pendulous, or essentially so, but in some species of *Cymbidium, Catasetum, Cyrtopodium, Grammatophyllum,*

WM. KIRCH—ORCHIDS, LTD.

Vanda x Fairy Queen. Note the root system of this example of monopodial orchid.

and others, many of the roots (or branches therefrom) grow straight upward, frequently forming a sort of basket into which falling leaves and other potentially fertilizing substances may lodge. The white, threadlike, copiously branched root systems of several species of

Rodriguezia and *Ionopsis*, certain Oncidiums of the *O. sphacelatum* alliance, and others, grow into a dense tangle which forms a characteristic and distinctive feature of these orchids.

The roots of most species of the monopodial genus *Phalaenopsis* become considerably flattened as they creep over surfaces, and they cling with extraordinary tenacity. Further, in those species of *Vanda*, *Aerides*, and others whose leaves are markedly terete, the roots assist the plants to clamber from the dense undergrowth of the jungle up to the tops of high trees in search of the light they require for blossoming.

Pseudobulbs

The stems or pseudobulbs of orchids offer a virtually inexhaustible series of variations. Even within the same genus, tremendous differences in dimensions and shapes of these structures are to be found. For example, all of the Cattleyas related to *C. labiata* possess distinctly bulky, rather spindle-shaped pseudobulbs, while the bifoliate Cattleyas, such as *C. bicolor* and *C. guttata*, are characterized by elongate, cylindrical stems which are, only for the sake of convenience, still called pseudobulbs. In the hundreds of different orchids found in the subtribe *Pleurothallidinae*, the stems are in many cases so reduced as to be almost unnoticed save by the careful observer. In the gigantic genera *Epidendrum* and *Dendrobium*, both true stems and pseudobulbs are found. In certain Bulbophyllums (for example, *B. minutissimum*) distinct pseudobulbs are found, but they are scarcely larger than a pinhead. Contrarily, in the fabulous *Grammatophyllum speciosum*, the pseudobulbs may attain lengths in excess of 25 feet.

Leaf Differences

The leaves of monopodial orchids offer further extremes of variation. While they are usually longer than broad, they fluctuate tremendously in texture, from almost paper-thin to excessively rigid and fleshy. In most orchids which have deciduous foliage the leaves are relatively fragile in texture, furnished with a distinct stalk, and more or less plaited or folded. The margins of almost all orchid leaves are entire, though in *Cattleyopsis*, *Broughtonia*, and a few species of *Oncidium* definite saw-tooth indentations are to be found.

Inflorescences

In the sympodial orchids, the inflorescence is of almost every conceivable type. Solitary, more or less stalked flowers are found in many genera, such as *Lycaste, Maxillaria,* most Masdevallias, *Huntleya,* etc. Short, few-flowered racemes obtain in many entire genera or sections of genera; elongated many-flowered racemes are found in others; and in some groups (such as *Arpophyllum* and *Oberonia*), dense, compact

A flowering specimen of *Bulbophyllum cupreum.* Note the creeping rhizomes characteristic of this species.

C. E. POULSEN

spikes are present. The panicle is well developed in, for example, the section *Cyrtochilum* of *Oncidium,* in which the flower-spikes often attain lengths in excess of 15 feet. In the large section *Megaclinium* of *Bulbophyllum* (formerly maintained as a distinct genus), the floral axis or rachis is prominently flattened, with the flowers produced from the flat sides of this often extraordinarily developed, frequently colored structure.

THE ORCHID FLOWER

Though orchids are generally conceded to be the most highly developed of flowering plants, the basic arrangement of their blossoms is remarkably simple, when one takes the time to examine them with care. All orchid flowers essentially consist of seven floral parts—three sepals, three petals, and the column or *gynostemium*. The lip or *labellum*, in most cases the showiest part of the blossom, is actually a highly modified petal, and not a separate structure at all, as many persons

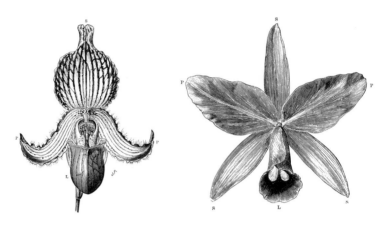

Left, *Paphiopedilum Fairrieanum*. The parts of the flower of this typical "Lady's-Slipper" orchid are indicated by the letter "s" for the sepals, "p" for the petals, and "l" for the lip. The dorsal sepal is easily identified but the joined lateral sepals are barely visible behind the lip. Right, *Cattleya Bowringiana*. The three sepals, two petals, and the lip of the flower of this typical orchid are indicated.

suppose. In the descriptions in Part III of this book, however, the lip is considered separately from the petals.

In the drawing of *Cattleya Bowringiana* one can see that the three outer segments of the typical orchid flower are the sepals. Beneath these, the ovary (which contains the flower's potential seeds) appears like the stalk, or pedicel, of the flower. More will be said of this later. In certain genera or species (for example, some kinds of *Pleurothallis*, *Bulbophyllum*, and *Oncidium*) the two lower sepals, which are the lateral ones, are combined into a single structure.

The petals consist of two identical, generally larger, floral parts borne inside the sepals, plus the lip, which may be of almost any conceivable form, and which is characteristically the lowermost and most spectacular segment of all. The lip may be tubular (as in *Cattleya* and certain species of *Laelia, Trichopilia, Sobralia,* and *Phaius*), expanded into a broad area with complicated warts and protuberances (*Oncidium* and *Odontoglossum,* among others), or it may be almost indistinguishable from the other petals (as in *Masdevallia, Pleurothallis,* and *Stelis*). This lip should be uppermost in the flower, but by an extremely complicated torsion or twisting of the pedicellate ovary, often to 180° (and in some rare instances even to 360°), it characteristically becomes the lowermost floral segment. In some orchid genera, such as *Polystachya,* the lip is uppermost in the blossom; the flower is then termed *nonresupinate* as opposed to the normal (for orchids) resupinate condition.

The column is the reproductive part of the orchid blossom, and is the primary feature distinguishing the Orchidaceae from all other families of plants. The column contains the female (pistillate) and male (staminate) sexual organs of the flower. The pistillate or female part consists of a sticky-surfaced, rather convex area called the *stigma* or stigmatic surface. In orchids the staminate element, the pollen, is generally not separated into tiny grains, as in a lily or geranium, for example, but is formed into compact, more or less waxy masses, termed *pollinia.* The grains are present nevertheless, though indistinguishable. Pollination of an orchid flower (explained in greater detail on pages 251 to 253) is effected by placing one or more of the pollinia on this stigma. The microscopic tubes produced by the individual grains of the pollen-masses grow down through the short upper portion of the ovary cavity to fertilize the ovules, which are found there in tremendous quantities.

With few exceptions, the pollinia are borne in a single anther, at or near the apex of the column. The number of pollinia, which may be two, four, six, or eight, is often a critical determining factor in the genera comprising the orchid family. *Laelia,* for example, is primarily distinguished from *Cattleya* by having eight pollinia rather than four. *Eria* has eight pollinia, and thereby differs from *Dendrobium,* which has four, and so on.

Exception to the Rule

The single group of orchids that differs from the others in the technical characters of the column consists of four rather small genera of the *Cypripedium* alliance (subtribe *Cypripedilinae*). These genera are usually placed in a separate subfamily called the *Diandrae*, as opposed to all other orchids, which are in the subfamily *Monandrae*. Some authorities have even suggested that this group would be better relegated to a separate family, to rank next to the Orchidaceae. This is because these plants—generally considered to be the most archaic of all orchids—possess two fertile anthers instead of the single one found in

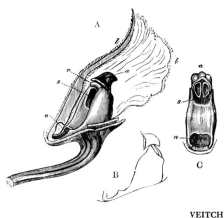

Dendrobium chrysanthum. In this drawing the parts of the orchid are indicated by "a" for the anther, "r" for the rostellum, "s" for the stigma, "l" for the lip, and "n" for the nectary.

A. Lateral view of the flower with the anther in its proper position before the ejection of the pollinia. All the perianth segments are removed except the lip which is longitudinally bisected. B. Outline of the column viewed laterally after the anther has ejected the pollinia. C. Front view of the column showing the empty cells of the anther after it has ejected its pollinia. The anther is represented hanging too low and covering more of the stigma than it actually does.

all other members of the family. A third anther is also present, technically, in the *Cypripedium* group, but it is sterile and altered to form a prominent, usually shield-shaped structure called a *staminode* or *staminodium* (see figure, page 21). This staminode is located at the tip of the column, and is variously shaped, often being lobed and furnished with tiny warts or hairs. It is frequently an important diagnostic character in the identification of closely related species. The staminode acts as a protective covering for the anthers—which are borne on each side of the usually broad column—and the stigma, which lies between them.

Variations in Orchid Flowers

Tremendous variability occurs in the floral structure of orchids, both naturally and because of genetic or artificial forces. Abnormally shaped flowers are frequently found. Excessive interbreeding seems to have a marked effect upon the appearance of these freak blossoms in certain groups; floral aberrations and cultural idiosyncracies both seem overly common when this takes place.

Catasetum viridiflavum plant with staminate (male) inflorescence.

H. TEUSCHER

Within genera, even within species, a condition known as *dimorphism* takes place. This is an extremely interesting and neglected phase of orchidology, one which merits much further study. For example, in *Catasetum* all species (with the exception of the few members of the section *Clowesia*) generally have unisexual flowers, which in most instances differ so radically from each other, male from female, that they have often been described as completely separate entities. In *Cycnoches*, the marvelous "Swan Orchids," essentially the same condition prevails. In *Dimorphorchis Lowii*, *Grammatophyllum speciosum*, *G. scriptum*, *G. Measuresianum*, and a few other orchids, a remarkable situation of floral dimorphy occurs, in which either sterile blossoms (as in the case of the Grammatophyllums) with abortive sexual parts and, generally, no labellum, or a widely divergent color phase (as in the *Dimorphorchis*) is found. Although no definite reason for this dimorphic condition has as yet been ascertained, it is thought to have some connection with the pollination of the flowers by insects or other flying creatures.

To quote the "Father of Orchidology," John Lindley: "There is no order of plants the structure of whose flowers is so anomalous as regards the relation borne by the parts of reproduction, or so singular in respect to the form of the floral envelope. Unlike most endogenous plants, the calyx and corolla are not similar to each other in form, texture and color (as in the Lily, Crocus, Narcissus, Squill, Amaryllis, etc.); neither have they any similitude to the changes of outline that are met with in such irregular flowers as are produced in other families of the Vegetable Kingdom. On the contrary, by an excessive development and singular conformation of one of the petals, called the labellum or lip, by irregularities either of form, size or direction of the other sepals and petals, by the peculiar adhesion of those parts to each other, and by the occasional suppression of a portion of them, flowers are produced so unusual and so grotesque in form that it is no longer with the Vegetable Kingdom that they can be compared, but we are forced to seek resemblances in the animal world."[1]

The segments of the orchid flower—the sepals, petals, and lip—are, in truth, incredibly diverse in their structure. In many instances they differ radically from species to species within a single genus.

Even the pollinia, in which the pollen grains are grouped, commonly in astronomical numbers, may be pear-shaped, disclike, or almost rounded. In most orchids they are lodged in a special concave depression at or near the apex of the column, which is called the *clinandrium*. They are covered by an often complex hooded structure called the *anther-cap*. The pollinia are usually accompanied by a strap-shaped appendage generally known as the *caudicle*.

The sepals or outermost series of perianth segments of the orchid flower, are generally uniform, but numerous deviations from the equality and similarity of the three occur. The most common deviant is seen in the upper (dorsal) sepal, which is quite often of a different size and shape from the lateral pair; examples are to be found in the genus *Renanthera*, the peculiar section *Restrepia* of *Pleurothallis*, section *Cirrhopetalum* of *Bulbophyllum*, and in many Oncidiums. In

[1] *English Cyclopaedia* 4:3. 1832.

Masdevallia, for the most part, the three sepals are united at their bases into a tube (called the sepaline tube), and at the free ends are prolonged into more or less elongate tails (termed *caudae*).

The equality of the two petals is constant, but their size may vary greatly in relation to the rest of the flower. In *Masdevallia* and some allied genera and most Bulbophyllums, they are often reduced to minute structures scarcely apparent to the casual eye. Conversely, in a few of

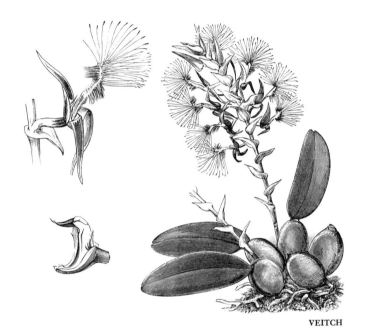

VEITCH

Bulbophyllum barbigerum

the rarer "Lady's-Slippers," such as *Paphiopedilum Sanderianum* and *Phragmipedium caudatum*, the petals are attenuated into ribbonlike tails one to two feet in length.

The lip is by far the most important of the orchid flower's perianth segments, and it is also the most variable in form. Into whatever form it has been molded (and in no two genera is it precisely alike, also varying considerably from species to species in each sizable generic assemblage), its structure is always such as to secure the greatest efficiency in aiding the fertilization of the flower. The lip is usually attached to the column by a short claw, which is sometimes so delicately hinged on it that the lip-blade vibrates on the slightest movement of air. A remarkable case of this oscillatory motion is afforded by the labellum of *Bulbophyllum barbigerum,* which even in the most tranquil greenhouse is almost constantly in motion. In *Epidendrum* this lip-claw is more or less joined to the column; in *Odontoglossum* it is simply parallel to it, while in *Oncidium* and many other genera it is at right angles to it. In *Isochilus* and a few other genera we find the labellum in its simplest form, and basically similar to the petals; on the other

One of the fabulous modern white *Phalaenopsis* hybrids.

hand, in *Coryanthes, Stanhopea,* and allied groups it is of such amazingly complex structure that its description in mere words is virtually impossible. In many genera the lip is prolonged into a slender spur, which in *Angraecum sesquipedale* reaches a length only slightly less than one foot. A sac or pouch of varying size and shape is common in many orchids, reaching its greatest development in the "slippers" of the *Cypripedium* alliance, and in several species of *Catasetum.* Tubular labella are well known from their appearance in most Cattleyas and Laelias. The magnificent intricate fringe developed on the lip-margins of *Rhyncholaelia Digbyana* has caused this species to be widely used in breeding. On the lip is often found a fleshy excrescence or *callus,* which in many orchids is of very complex structure (*Oncidium* gives a good example); in other genera the callus is reduced to small tubercles or simple keels or raised lines which, in some species of *Odontoglossum* and throughout *Coelogyne* and *Thunia*, are beautifully fringed. In most members of the *Huntleya* group the callus or crest of the lip is thickened and often intricately furrowed.

The column also varies considerably in form, but except in the members of the subtribe *Cypripedilinae*, the deviations from the general type arise chiefly from the enlargement or diminution of the various parts. Appendages of different sorts are often found on the column, these in such genera as *Oncidium* often reaching considerable development. In *Huntleya* and certain allied genera the column is broad and thick, equaling in breadth the fleshy crest of the labellum; in marked contrast to this is the long, slender, curving column of the male flowers of *Cycnoches*, which bear a striking resemblance to a swan's graceful neck. There are many additional variations in the column structure, some of them subtle, others startling in their divergence from the norm.

ECONOMIC IMPORTANCE OF ORCHIDS

Orchids are of importance primarily for their highly valued flowers. Four genera and their closely allied groups are responsible for the great majority of types commercially grown today, although there are somewhat in excess of 660 known genera. A large proportion of these groups are rare or seldom seen in cultivation, and are often of interest only to the connoisseur or to the botanist.

The production of flowers and plants for sale is a multimillion-dollar annual business in the United States alone. Some firms around our large cities produce hundreds of thousands of orchid flowers each year, the largest numbers being cut at the various holidays. In addition to this obvious commercial value, orchids are of considerable importance to man in other, less well known fashions.

Vanilla planifolia is the original source of commercial vanilla extract. This culinary product is obtained from the dried, cured seed capsules which develop—usually as a result of hand-pollination—after the viny plant has produced a succession of rather showy, fragrant, Cattleya-shaped greenish flowers.

Other species of the genus *Vanilla* (notably *V. Pompona*) are also capable of producing vanillin, the alkaloid used in the extract, but they

In Hawaii the growing of orchids is one of the most important industries.

are of somewhat inferior quality and have not been utilized on any extensive commercial scale.

Salep can be obtained in almost any drugstore, but most people do not realize that it is the product of certain orchids, notably some species of the genus *Orchis*, native in Europe. The fleshy, succulent tubers are dried and ground, and when the resultant substance is mixed with water, it forms a widely-utilized bland food of great nutritive value.

Many other orchids are used, with greater or lesser frequency, as foodstuffs. For example, in olden days—before commercial and overly-zealous amateur collectors had virtually exterminated the plants in many areas—several of the magnificent and highly prized "Jewel Orchids" of the genus *Anoectochilus* were sold in the native markets of Malaya and Indonesia, the succulent leaves being used as vegetables. In the same area, dried pieces of the leaves of *Dendrobium salaccense* were cooked with rice, to which they imparted a delicate and exotic flavor. The young fruits of the Indo-Malayan *Vanilla Griffithii* are

OSCAR M. KIRSCH   REG S. DAVIS

Left, a large commercial orchid establishment in Hawaii, filled with hundreds of flowering plants of various kinds. Right, *Vanda x Miss Joaquim.* Probably the most widely cultivated orchid in the world. In Hawaii it is grown in such quantities that the flowers are sold by the pound!

even today eaten as a delicacy, the flavor being described as particularly sweet.

"Faham Tea" was a popular beverage during the Victorian Age. This, too, is the product of an orchid, being the dried and cured foliage of the handsome *Jumellea fragrans*, a native of the Mascarene Islands. Tea has also been prepared from the pseudobulbs and/or foliage of members of such diverse genera as *Bletia, Renanthera*, and even *Cattleya*. These brews are generally used for medicinal purposes.

Shortly after the first colonists arrived in North America, the Indians taught them the uses of various herbs as medicines and foods. Among these plants were several species of "Lady's-Slipper Orchids" (genus

Cypripedium); their roots were boiled with a small amount of some sweet substance—such as maple sugar—and the resulting broth was drunk for headaches and other simple ills. Some orchids, notably *Epipactis latifolia*, were brought from Europe by the early settlers for medicinal uses, and have now become established in several parts of the United States.

Orchids of such genera as *Oberonia, Dendrobium, Eria, Bulbophyllum, Thrixspermum, Eulophia, Geodorum, Grammatophyllum,* and *Hetaeria* are used medicinally in various parts of the world, the stems, leaves, pseudobulbs, flower-buds, or expanded blossoms being crushed or boiled for this purpose.

A few kinds of orchids exert a religious or superstitious influence over the native inhabitants in some parts of the globe. In Borneo, *Coelogyne asperata* is held to be sacred, and collection of it is fraught with difficulty. In parts of Malaya, *Cymbidium Finlaysonianum* is used as a talisman to keep evil spirits away from the native villages, and the roots of the same orchid are chewed and sprinkled over a sick elephant. The Moluccans make a supposedly all-powerful love philter from the seeds of *Grammatophyllum scriptum*, which is common in their islands.

In the Philippines, Indonesia, and New Guinea the flexible stems of some kinds of *Dendrobium* are used in weaving and basketry. In the interior mountains of New Guinea many of the primitive tribesmen wear intricate bracelets woven from the yellow, stemlike pseudobulbs of *Dendrobium utile* and certain allied species.

Geodorum nutans in the Philippines and certain members of *Cyrtopodium* in Brazil furnish glues which are widely used, particularly in the manufacture of musical instruments, such as guitars. The substance is obtained from the fleshy tubers or pseudobulbs. In parts of Central America, the inflated, hollow pseudobulbs of *Laelia* (*Schomburgkia*) *tibicinis* are fashioned into crude horns or trumpets, which are blown during certain special religious ceremonies.

HISTORY OF EARLY ORCHID CULTIVATION

Although a few Cymbidiums had been grown by the Chinese for centuries, it was not until about 1731 that the first orchidaceous plant entered Western collections. This was *Bletia purpurea*, which was sent to the English gardener Peter Collinson in that year from the Bahamas. A few years later, one or more species of *Vanilla* were introduced into English collections but, like all orchids at that time, they were chronically mistreated and usually perished before producing their flowers. Indeed, attempts to cultivate orchids under the artificial conditions found in European greenhouses were generally disappointing. This was in large part due to the fact that gardeners of the era did not have any idea of the correct cultural methods to apply to their plants, so that the mortality rate among newly introduced specimens was discouragingly high.

In 1778, Dr. John Fothergill brought live plants of *Phaius Tankervilliae* and *Cymbidium ensifolium* from China, and the *Phaius* was induced to flower shortly after. *Epidendrum cochleatum* first bloomed in England in 1787, and the next year a specimen of *E. fragrans* flowered at the Royal Botanic Gardens, Kew. These Epidendrums were grown "in pots of earth composed of rotten wood and decayed leaves, plunged into the tan bed of a pit." It is a wonder they even survived, let alone blossomed.

By 1794, some 15 species of epiphytic orchids were being grown with more or less success at Kew, almost all of them natives of the West Indian region; these included *Epidendrum ciliare, Isochilus linearis, Lycaste Barringtoniae, Maxillaria coccinea, Oncidium altissimum,* and *O. carthagenense.* At this time all were considered to be members of the great catch-all genus of the period, *Epidendrum.* Their collectors had noted that they were found growing in trees, hence it was assumed that they were parasites, an erroneous idea which has persisted to the present day. These unfortunate epiphytes were, therefore, generally potted in a mould formed of decayed wood and leaves, although occasionally a medium of loam and peat was utilized. The pots were then plunged into beds formed of rotten foliage and bark, and subjected to extremes of high temperatures and sodden moisture at all times. Despite this crude and cruel treatment, many of the plants managed to survive for long periods of time, thus giving added evidence of the striking durability of the orchid.

The foundation of the Horticultural Society of London in 1809 gave a tremendous impetus to horticulture in general in England, and in part because of its existence, orchids came to be considered as not just curiosities, but botanical subjects for serious attention. The first English firm to grow orchids for sale was Messrs. Loddiges, who imported a

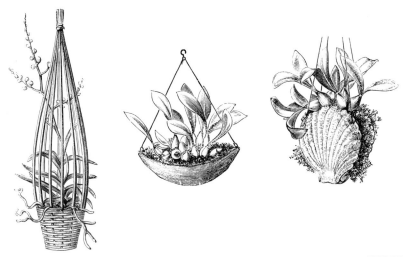

VEITCH

An orchid basket used by Sir Joseph Banks in the year 1817. The plant is the rare *Sarcanthus paniculatus*. Center and right, two types of orchid containers used by Messrs. Loddiges, early English orchid-growers, about 1840. The large shells on the right should be particularly noted.

large number of different species from abroad for cultivation in their large nurseries at Hackney.

Epiphytic orchids in particular presented great difficulties to the early growers, and almost the only person to keep one of these "air plants" alive for any protracted period of time was a Mr. Fairbairn, who succeeded in flowering *Aerides odoratum* in 1813. His remarkable treatment of epiphytic species is quoted as follows, from the *Transactions of the Horticultural Society of London* for that year: "I put the plant when first received into a basket with old tan [tan-bark] and moss and hung it up in the pine house where it was exposed to the summer sun and to the fire-heat in winter. A tub of water was placed near it into which I could plunge the basket six or seven times a day, or as often as I passed it."

Cylindrical wicker baskets were adopted by Sir Joseph Banks in the 1820's, and many of the more robust epiphytic orchids thrived in the compost of "vegetable mould and moss" with which they were filled. About this time, Loddiges used a potting-medium of "rotten wood and moss with a small quantity of sand." The greenhouses in which the orchids were kept were "heated by brick flues to as high a temperature as could be obtained by that means, and by a tan bed in the middle kept constantly moist by watering and from which a steamy evaporation was rising at all times without any ventilation from without."

John Lindley proposed a series of cultural recommendations for orchids in 1830, suggestions which were followed blindly by growers for many years thereafter—with characteristically disastrous results, since he proposed a constantly excessive humidity and as great amounts of heat as could be attained in the greenhouse. These heated glass enclosures of the time were known as "stoves"—a fitting term for them!

About 1835 a critical reform in orchid culture was proposed by two men, Joseph Cooper, gardener to Earl Fitzwilliam at Wentworth, Yorkshire, and Joseph Paxton, gardener to the Duke of Devonshire at Chatsworth. Paxton, in particular through the pages of his *Magazine of Botany* (which ran from 1834 to 1849), exerted a tremendous influence on the orchid enthusiasts of his day, because of his notable success with these "impossible parasites." Lindley visited Chatsworth in 1838 and recorded his impressions as follows: "The success with which epiphytes are cultivated by Mr. Paxton is wonderful, and the climate in which this is effected, instead of being so hot and damp that the plants can only be seen with as much peril as if one had to visit them in an Indian jungle, is as mild and delightful as that of Madeira." Paxton's system basically consisted of the following points: separate houses or portions of houses for orchids from different climates; a lower average temperature than was maintained by other growers, admission of more fresh air into the houses, especially while the plants were actively growing; maintenance of a moist, humid atmosphere by periodic wetting of the paths and growing-stages of the houses; and better drainage, with consequent better root development through an improved system of potting.

Gradually, as decades passed, orchids became more numerous in both private and public collections, as their cultivation grew simplified through better understanding of their basic requirements. In the latter part of the nineteenth century, a veritable orchid craze swept England and parts of the Continent. Plants were gathered by the hundreds of thousands from tropical areas such as the Colombian Andes, India,

Malaya, and the Philippines by professional collectors sent out by the great commercial firms of the era. Astounding prices were paid for particularly rare or choice species or variants, and collections containing upwards of one million specimens were not unknown. Unhappily,

The Cattleya House at the Royal Exotic Nursery, King's Road, Chelsea, England, around 1875. Note the many-flowered basket of Dendrobiums on the far left and the giant "strap-leaved" Vandas scattered down the main bench of Cattleyas.

tremendous numbers of the plants gathered in the wild were lost in transit to Europe, and in certain areas—notably in South America—desirable types were almost or totally exterminated.

Hybrid orchids began to make their appearance in abundance about the beginning of this century. Whereas fifty years ago the average collection consisted almost exclusively of species, today the situation is exactly reversed, and hybrids are vastly more widely cultivated than wild species.[1]

[1] See pages 239 to 240 for a history of orchid hybrids and breeding.

II

Culture

GENERAL CULTURAL NOTES

The basic horticultural requirements of most orchids are rather similar. Each genus, however, and often each species and variant within that genus, has its particular necessities under the artificial conditions of cultivation. Even so, no matter how detailed we make observations on culture, it would still be patently impossible to deal with all variations, for every orchid plant is an individual, and is subject to an individual's vagaries.

Air

One of the prime requisites of a successful orchid collection, whether a modest or an extensive one, whether kept indoors or in a fine greenhouse, is sufficient air. Most of the commonly cultivated orchids are air-plants by nature, and as such require quantities of fresh, freely moving air at all times. During the early days of orchid growing, it was the practice to place the plants in closed, stuffy glasshouses; orchids will grow under such adverse conditions (they will grow under virtually any conditions), but the collector will encounter fewer major difficulties if his plants are allowed ample air. Many types of tropical orchids, such as *Vanda*, *Phalaenopsis*, and *Aerides*, with their prominently developed aerial roots, do best if grown in baskets hung from the beams or cross-pieces of the greenhouse or lath-house; in this way they are more exposed to air currents than if placed in pots on a crowded bench.

Light

Different orchids require differing amounts of light. In general they should be furnished with large quantities of diffused (very seldom direct) sunlight. Although in nature orchids are often found growing exposed to full sunlight (as on bare rock outcroppings, or in the fringes of woods where the light potential is high), when brought into cultivation caution must be exercised to prevent burning of the foliage. Certain orchids, however, do not flower properly unless they are almost completely exposed to the sun. Other orchids grow in situations where at least part of the day they are given quantities of semidiffused light (as in clearings in a dense forest). Few of these plants are ever discovered in the excessively shaded, stagnant interiors of jungles, where light and freely moving air are both at a premium.

Heating

Heating is a factor allied to light, since sunshine furnishes much of the natural warmth to the collection during many months of the year. Orchids are often spoken of as hothouse plants; this is in large part incorrect, and sometimes dangerously so, since most of them rebel at excessive heat. From the viewpoint of temperature requirements the family is basically divided into three major groups. The ideal night temperatures of these groups are as follows:

Cool: 45–50° F.   Intermediate: 55–65° F.   Hot (or warm): 65° F. and above.

In the main, all orchid genera may be placed in one or the other of these categories, although certain large groups must be distributed over two or more of the categories, because of the tremendous distributional ranges of the component species. Temperature requirements are indicated for each of the genera and species treated in Part III of this book.

Moisture

Watering of orchids and humidity in the air about them are highly important considerations for the grower. Probably the commonest error made by beginners is the tendency to overwater the plants. Orchids, with few exceptions, thrive better if watered moderately and allowed to become relatively dry between waterings. While in their native habitats these plants are rained upon almost daily (at least during certain seasons of the year), they are soon dried off by the heat of the sun. But the medium in which the plants are potted—whether osmunda, tree-fern fiber, or one of the new bark preparations—is in itself a moisture-retaining substance, and although it may appear superficially dry the day after a heavy soaking, careful inspection will probably reveal that the pot or basket is still sufficiently moist for the plant's well-being. Under artificial conditions, therefore, watering every day may prove to be a fatal error.

Natural rain water is ideal for orchids, but it is seldom available to growers. In general the water supply of the community is acceptable. Caution should be taken during the chill winter months that cold water is not put on the plants. If necessary, hot water may be added to that from the tap, so that a temperature of about 50–60° F. is obtained.

Watering, generally speaking, is an individual problem with the orchidist. A little observation makes it possible to tell which orchids in the collection require more moisture than others, and which pots or baskets dry out faster than others. The texture of the compost is a good criterion for determination of what to water, and at what intervals of frequency. If the potting-medium feels moist to the touch, water should be withheld, but when it seems dry, water may be given. Plants grown in baskets or on rafts or slabs, with their compost more or less exposed, require more water than those in pots. During the cloudy winter months, watering generally needs to be done only once or twice a week, whereas in the summer, watering every other day—sometimes every day—may be necessary.

When watering the collection with a garden hose, a rather fine spray or light stream should be used, to avoid hitting the plants with too much force; this is particularly important when they are potted in one of the bark mixtures, at least until the plants are so well established that the roots hold them firmly in place. There are now available on the market several devices called "water-breakers," which effectively split up the stream of water—even at full force—so that it falls softly on the plants.

Humidity is easily maintained in the enclosed greenhouse—and to a somewhat lesser degree in the lath-house—by careful arrangement of moisture-retaining accessory plants under the benches, use of absorbent gravel or pumice on the floor, spraying the air and benches during the day, and by other means. Automatic humidifiers are commonly built into greenhouses designed for orchid culture, and their use is highly recommended.

Resting

Resting is the term applied to that period of the life-cycle when the active growth of the plant is completed and matured, flowering is (in most cases) finished, and a period of relative dormancy begins. These periods of rest usually coincide with the dry season in the plant's country of origin.

The need for a rest varies from genus to genus, and often from species to species within a given genus. Many orchids grow throughout the year, hence no rest-period need be given these. In general, resting plants should have a greatly reduced supply of water, increased circulation of air, and a slightly cooler temperature. Comments on individual requirements for rest-periods are given in the discussions of the genera in Part III.

Fertilizing

In the past it was often stated by authorities of the day that orchids did not require fertilizing. We now know that this is not true. A regular schedule of application of fertilizing materials is strongly recommended for even the smallest collection. The results are vastly increased vegetative growth and flower production. Many fertilizing agents are available for the orchidist's use, ranging from several animal manures to a number of materials manufactured expressly for orchids. Since many orchids are now being grown in bark preparations, or mixtures containing them, a fertilizer that is high in available nitrogen is particularly recommended. How often these should be applied is largely determined by the inclination of the individual grower. Best results, however, are generally obtained when the entire collection is fertilized at about bi-weekly intervals.

HOUSING THE ORCHID COLLECTION

"Where shall I keep my orchids?" is the initial question of the beginner. Housing varies in scope from the small Wardian case to the gigantic ranges of greenhouses of the commercial establishment, with many thousands of specimens grown under acres of glass. In growing orchids, whether on a small or a large scale, the problem is to approximate, as closely as possible, the conditions under which the plants live in their native habitats. Often it will be found that orchids grown as cultivated plants will become larger and will produce finer and more numerous blossoms than those found in the wild, thus illustrating that with proper care, even Nature can be improved upon.

This discussion of housing is presented under three categories: greenhouse, lath-house, and Wardian case or other indoor apparatus. Obviously, the first and third methods may be used anywhere in the world, while the lath or slat-house is practical only in climes where moderate temperatures prevail during most of the year. In tropical countries, many orchids are grown out-of-doors. This situation is considered on pages 57 to 64.

Greenhouse

The beginner who wishes to grow orchids in a greenhouse, which is by far the most efficient arrangement for the collection, has two choices: he may either purchase a prefabricated structure, or he may construct one himself. In these times handsome and highly efficient greenhouses can be bought at reasonable prices from a number of local establishments found throughout the country. The size, shape, and construction of the greenhouse naturally depend in the main on the grower and his own particular requirements. Certain rules regarding construction should, however, be observed if orchids are to be cultivated successfully. Initially, the greenhouse must have adequate provisions for air circulation, since orchids require this above all else. The ventilators should always be large enough to provide a good sweep of air; yet, because of storms and winds, they should be at all times easily controllable. Secondly, humidity is a most necessary requirement for successful cultivation of these plants, and by careful planning of the greenhouse this may be greatly facilitated. A built-in spray system is an excellent addition to every orchid house. It finds particular use during the hot summer months. Space should, if possible, be allowed under the benches for arrangements of ornamental plants—ferns and others that are tolerant of shade—for these will not only enhance the appearance of the collection, but also help to hold humidity over a long period of time. Porous gravel, coke, pumice, or similar absorbent material should be used in some part of the house as a bedding material or for the walkways, again for the sake of humidity. Finally, care must be taken to place the greenhouse in a suitable position on the land; that is, not beneath large dense-leaved trees, which may give excessive shade and whose falling branches may knock out the glass panes during storms. Shade can always be furnished the plants, when necessary, by such means as slats, paint, vines, or the new Saran cloths, but sunlight is more difficult to capture.

MYRON KIMNACH

An artificial "tree" at the Botanical Garden of the University of California in Berkeley showing the manner in which orchids, bromeliads, and other epiphytes are utilized.

Lath-house

In warm or tropical regions, the lath- or slat-house is one of the most popular structures for housing the orchid collection. It is naturally much less expensive to build than the greenhouse with its steel or wooden framework, endless panes of glass, and usually complex heating and atmospheric systems. The construction of the lath-house may be as simple or as complicated as the grower wishes; its size depends largely upon the available area and the number of plants to be contained within it.

A good lath-house should above all be solidly constructed, with strong upright posts for support—preferably imbedded in cement in the ground—and with the laths fastened securely to avoid injury by the wind. Humidity is naturally somewhat more of a problem in the lath-house than in the greenhouse, though it may be maintained by efficient distribution of accessory foliage plants under the benches, and by adequate watering during dry weather. While ventilation is not the problem sometimes encountered in the closed greenhouse, care should be taken not to plant so many shrubs or trees around the lath-house, that circulation of air is restricted. Lath-houses may be built in such a way that they blend into the landscaping of the property with great effectiveness. In most areas, handsome prefabricated lath-houses of singularly sturdy construction are now available at low cost. These are recommended for the beginning hobbyist who lives in a warm region where lath-house cultivation of orchids is feasible.

Wardian Cases and Other Indoor Apparatus

For persons who live in metropolitan areas, where space is not generally available for a greenhouse, various alternatives are open. (See also pages 53 to 56 of this book for comments on orchids as house plants.) Most important of these is the Wardian case, now obtainable in

A compact indoor greenhouse, available commercially and admirably suited for growing orchids in the home.

The Orchid Journal

several commercial sizes and designs, such as the Orchidarium, "indoor greenhouse," etc. These usually small, glass-walled cases are furnished with a thermostatically controlled electrical heating system. They are generally made with a pan at the bottom in which water or moist gravel is kept to insure proper humidity. For the beginning grower of orchids who lacks either the space or the finances for a greenhouse or lath-house, these indoor apparatuses form a most satisfactory substitute.

COMPOSTS, POTTING METHODS, AND CONTAINERS

Virtually every orchid genus—and often almost every species within a given genus—has its own requirements for composts and potting. Only the basic points for handling adult orchid plants will be outlined here. Specific needs of different kinds of plants are mentioned in Part III of this book. The somewhat specialized requirements of seedlings are taken up on pages 82 to 86.

Substances for Compost

Orchids today are potted in a wide variety of differing types of media, or composts, depending upon whether they are terrestrial or epiphytic in habit. Most present-day orchidists grow the bulk of their epiphytic orchids in straight osmunda fiber. This material, which occurs in several grades and colors (yellow, brown, black, with varying durability and softness), is the intricate fibrous root-system of two types of ferns of the genus *Osmunda*, found in moist places, especially in the southern United States. Polypodium fiber, also a product of the root-system of a fern (this one generally epiphytic, however), is also used as a substitute for osmunda, particularly in European collections.

Such genera as *Paphiopedilum*, *Masdevallia*, *Pleurothallis*, and *Bulbophyllum*, as well as the majority of orchid seedlings, are often cultivated in a mixed compost of osmunda with some sphagnum moss added. This true moss, in itself an attractive, soft, fleshy plant, retains tremendous quantities of water over a long period; thus it is an ideal medium for plants that require a constant supply of moisture. The various species of the genus *Sphagnum* are native over all the world, growing mostly in boggy situations in more or less full shade.

Today many orchidists are turning to the use of the various kinds of tree-fern fiber, often known by its vernacular names of *hapuu* (in Hawaii), *xaxím* (in Brazil), or *malquique* (in Mexico). This virtually indestructible, rather harsh fiber is obtained from the trunks and basal root-masses of certain kinds of arborescent ferns which grow mostly in the mountains of tropical countries. Genera such as *Cibotium*, *Alsophila*, *Cyathea*, and *Hemitelia* furnish varying grades of this important material, which is today principally available through specialized American importers who obtain it from Mexico, Brazil, and Hawaii. Used as a potting compost, in the manner of osmunda, this tree-fern fiber is admirably suited for baskets and as individual rafts, since it is so durable that it may be cut or sawn like soft wood. One or another kind of the tree-fern fibers will persist in good condition for from three to more than ten years, under average greenhouse use.

Bark preparations are also used. They are discussed in a later chapter.

The majority of the epiphytic orchids in common cultivation— Cattleyas, Epidendrums of the pseudobulbous type, Dendrobiums, and many others—are probably best grown in ordinary clay flower pots. Glazed pots are not widely used, since they do not allow for sufficient aeration of the roots and compost. Though many other composts have been used from time to time, more and more of the expert orchidists are returning to the "old" potting-medium, osmunda fiber, which exhibits many striking benefits and few defects.

Potting with osmunda is not difficult, though some practice is needed in working with it. Initially, the drainage hole at the bottom of the pot should always be enlarged with a hammer or mallet, to assure the extra good drainage that is essential to success with any orchid plant. Approximately one-third to one-half of the total pot's depth should be filled with broken (not crushed) crock or brick, or large pieces of gravel. Some orchidists recommend the addition of chunks of charcoal, but in many areas it has been found that this increases the rate at which the osmunda deteriorates, and a stale compost occurs too soon. The osmunda fiber, first moistened for better manageability, is cut across the grain into chunks about 1½ to 3 inches square. The plant is then set in the partially crock-filled pot, and these chunks of osmunda are carefully worked in around the roots. The rhizome, or actual base of the plant, should never be covered with the fiber; if it is, this part of the plant may rot.

With the majority of the commonly grown orchid genera, the osmunda should be worked around the roots until a tight compost is obtained—so tight, in fact, that if the plant is picked up the pot remains affixed. Certain of the more delicate kinds of orchids require a somewhat less forceful potting than this. The top of the compost should be trimmed to a neat surface; then, if necessary, the plant should be tied to a wooden or metal stake. Finally, it should be carefully labeled.

Pots for Orchids

The hobbyist will ask the proper size of pot to use. The average life of osmunda fiber under normal conditions is about two years; the

GEORGE FULLER

Well-potted orchids. Left to right: *Pholidota conchoidea*, *Coelogyne Rossiana*, *Eria Rimanni*.

orchid plant should therefore be potted for a comparable period—that is, in a pot large enough to allow space for two growths, with the last one approaching the pot rim. If a plant has previously been in a 4-inch pot, for example, it should generally be transplanted into a 6-inch one.

It is inadvisable to use proportionately large pots, for the plants are then more difficult to care for, and excessive decomposition of the compost may result because of the increased watering necessary. Genera such as *Dendrobium*, *Lycaste*, and *Miltonia* usually take a smaller pot size than *Cattleya*, *Laelia*, or *Oncidium*, because their pseudobulbs grow closer together and it takes them longer to fill the available growing space. In repotting orchid plants, old shriveled roots should be clipped off, leaving mainly those that still retain their plumpness and apparent vitality. At the same time, as much of the stale compost as convenient should be teased away from the root-system.

Potting is best accomplished with a potting-stick, which can be purchased from most commercial orchid houses, or can easily be made from a piece of broom-handle. Pots should always be soaked and carefully cleaned in plain water before use. When orchids are to be potted, the plants should first be carefully inspected for insect pests or diseases, and these conditions should be remedied to avoid their extension into other parts of the collection.

After potting, special care is necessary for the plants until they have re-established themselves. In warm weather (the ideal time for potting to be done), the surface of the pot's compost should be dampened and the foliage lightly syringed with water. Such newly potted specimens should be kept in a warm, somewhat more shaded situation than usual, until the new green-tipped roots have started their growth; then the plant may be given an increase in water supply, though care should still be taken not to allow the osmunda to remain wet. As soon as the roots are obviously well on their way to becoming established again, the specimen may be treated as any mature plant.

Culture in Baskets

Many tropical epiphytic orchids, such as the numerous sarcanthad, or monopodial, genera—*Phalaenopsis*, *Vanda*, *Angraecum*, and others— are particularly well suited to basket culture, because of their abundant production of aerial roots and the elongate habit of the stems of many (except *Phalaenopsis*, the stems of which are notably abbreviated). The majority of types that may be grown successfully in baskets should be potted, not too firmly, in a straight compost of fresh osmunda fiber, preferably the brown kind rather than the more wiry black variety. Drainage, in the form of broken crock, is optional in most baskets, because of the open character of the container, but pieces may be added in small quantity if an especially well-aerated compost is desired.

Many orchids do well when grown in slatted baskets. This is the rare *Oncidium anthocrene* from Colombia and Panama.

Baskets

Orchid baskets, constructed especially for their cultivation, are now available from many commercial sources, both in this country and abroad. They are usually manufactured specifically for this purpose out of some hard, long-lasting, relatively moisture-impervious wood and the orchidist would do well to purchase these ready-made rather than attempt to construct his own.

Such orchid baskets are available in a variety of sizes and shapes so that almost every kind of plant regardless of size or formation can readily be accommodated within their confines.

The size of the basket naturally depends on the type of plant being placed within it; for example, a monopodial orchid, such as *Aerides odoratum* (which is an ideal subject for basket culture), growing only in a vertical plane and not spreading out horizontally (as in the sympodial orchids, such as *Cattleya* or *Epidendrum*) may be placed in a relatively small container, such as that shown on page 75. Such plants, once established—when the thick roots frequently attach themselves tightly to the frame of the basket—should not be repotted if this change can possibly be avoided. Rather, upon deterioration of the compost, the stale osmunda should be carefully pulled from around the root-system, and fresh chunks of the fiber worked in to take its place.

The treatment of the sympodially growing orchids when kept in baskets is somewhat different from that noted for the monopodials. Any species having a creeping, elongate rhizome will naturally, within a given time, exceed the limits of the compost in the basket. It should be then removed from the container, the old osmunda trimmed away as thoroughly as possible, and the plant either divided into smaller plants or repotted in a larger basket with fresh compost. Extra large specimens, when grown in baskets (or in pots, for that matter) are frequently difficult to attend to properly. Generally speaking, therefore, regular division of orchid plants in all instances should be undertaken for best results.

Special note should be made here of the several species of the genera *Stanhopea, Acineta, Gongora,* and such Peristerias as *P. cerina,* which are encountered in choice collections at this time. All of these strange and handsome epiphytes should be grown in baskets with extra large interstices between the cross-bars. This is obligatory because in this group of orchids the flower-spikes are produced from the base of the plant, and they grow almost straight downward before the blossoms are expanded. In a pot, these pendent inflorescences have been known to bury themselves in the compost and drainage, and open quite normally there.

Orchids on Rafts

Many orchids are conveniently cultivated on rafts or slabs of osmunda or tree-fern fiber, instead of in pots or baskets. Dwarf, prostrate, or clambering species are particularly well adapted to this mode of cultivation, which is mainly used in the warm greenhouse. Until the plants become fully established, they may be affixed to the compost by means of small staples made of bent galvanized wire of various gauges. Orchids grown on rafts in general require a more constantly moist atmosphere than those in pots or baskets, since the evaporation rate of the usually scanty compost is markedly higher. Especially during hot weather, raft-grown specimens should be sprayed with water at least twice daily, whether kept in the humidified greenhouse or outdoors: spraying may be lessened somewhat during cooler,

H. TEUSCHER

An orchid raft of cork bark with a flowering specimen of *Oncidium luridum*.

duller weather, but careful attention to the moisture-content of such rafts is always needed.

Formula for Terrestrials

Terrestrial (and the semiterrestrial) orchids in general require a single basic sort of potting medium, as indicated below. Variations on this basic recipe should be made for individual plants' requirements and for differing climatic conditions which demand larger or smaller quantities of humidity and heat. The base recipe for these ground-dwelling orchids is a well-drained mixture of about 1 part rich humus, 1 part well-decayed leaf-mould, 1 part chopped osmunda and sphagnum moss (or chopped tree-fern fiber and sphagnum moss), and ½ part dried cow or sheep manure. Whether grown in pots or in specially prepared outdoor beds, the terrestrial orchids invariably require perfect drainage, and generally will stand more full sunlight than many of their epiphytic relatives.

NO .

ORCHIDS AS HOUSE PLANTS

Since they are basically such sturdy plants, orchids may be grown almost anywhere in the home where sufficient light is available. They are admirably suited to window-shelves, sunny tables near picture windows or French doors, or to Wardian cases or special individual containers elsewhere throughout the house or apartment. Many enthusiasts successfully cultivate their precious plants on a window-sill, in the kitchen or living-room or dining-room, or even in the bath!

The beginner should notice, before starting his indoor home orchid collection, which types are particularly well suited for this sort of cultivation—for many are not. He would do well to begin with a few of the kinds indicated by an asterisk in the lists commencing on page 93 of this book. When he has successfully mastered their growth requirements—and has brought them into bloom *more than once*, thus indicating that he really understands their culture—he should go on to the others that are available.

The best possible position in a room is in a window, one that faces south (preferably), or east or west. Sun, more or less diffused by a light curtain, is an absolute necessity, especially so during the dim late fall and winter months. During the brighter spring and summer days the plants are easily subjected to too much light, and care must be taken that the foliage does not become burned. Fresh air is necessary in good quantity; but a chill draft should never blow directly on the plants.

All orchids benefit by greater exposure to light than to a smaller amount. Plants that have been grown in insufficient light are, granted, often more pleasing to the eye—a delightful clear shade of green, with sleek foliage and pseudobulbs—but they do not flower as well as those cultivated in bright light, and may not flower at all! However, when grown in a sunny window, the plants should not be closer than a foot from the glass, for too strong exposure will burn the usually fleshy foliage. In sufficiently warm climates, home-grown orchids will benefit considerably by being placed out-of-doors during the frost-free months. They may be left in the pots or baskets in which they have been kept indoors, and put in a rather sunny spot, perhaps under the edge of the shade furnished by a tree or large shrub. They should not receive too much exposure, though, as this will result in serious burning of the foliage and setback of the plants' growth.

The requirements of orchids as house plants are simple and few, and anyone—whether possessed of a "green thumb" or not—can successfully cultivate and bring into flower all but a few of the most difficult types. A few showy orchids can easily be added to any collection of plants in the home.

Most present-day apartments or houses have heating facilities that provide temperatures of 70–72° F. during the day and about 55–65° F. at night. This is an almost perfect range of heating for the majority of orchids.

Since the beginning grower should definitely concentrate on one special group of orchids—such as the intermediate, cool, or hot, or even one or more of the culturally allied genera such as *Laelia* and *Cattleya*, *Dendrobium* and *Oncidium*, or *Vanda* and *Phalaenopsis*— the temperature requirements of these plants will be approximately the same. It is possible to grow all of the three basic groups indoors, however, by careful placement of the plants. For example, the intermediate group (*Cattleya*, etc.)—which are especially recommended for the beginning hobbyist (see page 93)—will probably do best in one's living- or dining-room, where the temperatures are those preferred by the human inhabitants. The warm or hot types (*Phalaenopsis*, *Vanda*, etc.) will require a somewhat warmer spot, perhaps nearer a radiator or heating-vent, but with an abundant supply of light at all times. The cool group (*Odontoglossum*, many Miltonias, some Oncidiums, and others) should be kept in the coolest part of the house or apartment, although the position must still be well lighted by a window or glass doorway.

On chill winter nights a small lamp may be placed near the plants to give them a bit of added warmth, but the orchidist should take care not to burn the foliage or pseudobulbs by putting the heat too close to his prized specimens.

Even indoors, plants should always be given as much light as they will stand, short of burning. Plants that do not get enough light are gangling growers which seldom if ever produce flowers of top quality.

If a Wardian case or "indoor greenhouse" is being used, the side vents should be opened as frequently as possible, to allow the air to circulate freely. If the plants are being grown in pans on a table or window-sill, a nearby window or door should be opened during the day, so that the fresh air may flow around the plants.

Watering of orchids is largely a personal, individualized problem, depending on what kinds of plants are being grown, where they are being kept, what containers they are grown in, the type of compost used, and other factors. Normally, orchids grown as house plants dry out far more rapidly than those kept in the greenhouse or lath-house, because of the consistently drier atmosphere of the home. If one's plants are being cultivated in an "indoor greenhouse" or other enclosed space—where the available humidity is higher than on an exposed window-sill or table—they will require noticeably less water than otherwise.

Orchids with pseudobulbs (which act as storage organs for moisture) in general do not require as much water as do the bulbless types, such as Paphiopedilums, Vandas, Phalaenopsis, and others. Orchids cultivated in baskets or on rafts or tree-fern slabs require more water than those in pots. Certain orchids—members of the genera *Paphiopedilum, Phalaenopsis, Odontoglossum,* for example—should never be allowed to dry out, or the health of the plant will be seriously impaired. If the side of a pot (or the compost in it) feels cool and even vaguely moist to the touch, the plant is probably not in need of water, but if the compost or pot surface is warm and harsh-feeling, some moisture should be furnished. The osmunda or other material around the plant should never become brittle with dryness, as it is difficult to remoisten in such a state. When watering a plant—whether in a pot or basket, or on a slab or raft—the compost should be soaked thoroughly at least once a week (more often or less as required) and then allowed to dry out almost completely. Unless the plants are being grown under glass, as in a greenhouse, watering should never be done each day, as this tends to make the compost grow stale, to the detriment of the plant's health.

Humidity is often a problem indoors, particularly with a central heating system, which tends to dry out the air. This lack of humidity, however, is easily remedied by growing all of the plants in shallow trays, dishes, or pans. Half of a regular brick is placed in the middle of the pan, which is then filled with gravel or crushed porous pumice around the brick and with water to about two-thirds the depth of the gravel or pumice. The pan, containing the brick, gravel, and water, is placed on the window-sill or table in front of a window; the potted

The lovely "Lady's-Slipper" orchids of the genus *Paphiopedilum* grow as well as house plants. The pot should be set on a layer of moist gravel.

ROD MC LELLAN COMPANY

orchid plant is set on the brick, above the damp gravel. The water level in the gravel-filled pan should be maintained at as constant a level as possible, but should always be below the bottom of the pot in which the orchid is growing. If a basket, raft, or tree-fern slab is being used instead of a pot, the same arrangement may naturally be followed.

Through attention to these few simple rules, and perhaps with a little experimentation in one's own particular situation, the beginner can readily grow orchids in the house. I want to emphasize again that orchids are not difficult to grow. If any plants at all are being grown indoors, orchids may be added to them with notable success.

OUTDOOR CULTIVATION OF ORCHIDS

Many orchidists throughout the world grow at least part of their collections out-of-doors, with great success. Whether or not orchids may be grown outside depends largely, of course, on the climate, particularly when tropical species are concerned. There are large numbers of terrestrial orchids (and some epiphytic and lithophytic ones, notably from high mountain areas such as the Himalayas) that are hardy almost anywhere. There are, as well, a great many so-called tropical kinds that will survive and thrive under seemingly adverse conditions in temperate areas. In warm countries, naturally, almost all orchids may be grown outdoors, without any particular sort of special protection from the elements.

In temperate areas, such as most of the United States, Great Britain, and Central Europe, many growers place most of their orchids outdoors, under trees or shrubs, during the summer months. This is a highly recommended practice; the plants nearly always respond with greater exuberance than when confined to the greenhouse year-round. Care must be taken, of course, to expose the greenhouse-grown plants gradually to the brighter outdoor light; otherwise serious burning of the foliage and pseudobulbs may result. Careful attention must also be given to watering; fine sprayings outdoors are especially advantageous during warm weather.

Orchids that are kept outdoors year-round may be grown on trees, or rocks, or in garden beds. They may also be cultivated in pots, in hanging baskets, or on slabs for porch or terrace decoration. In such containers, the same general rules apply as for similar orchids in a lath-house.

Growing Orchids on Trees

Orchid enthusiasts who are fortunate enough to live in warm countries generally have, in addition to a wide variety of handsome native types growing wild at their very doorsteps, the added attraction of a climate moderate enough to grow a large number of their plants on trees. Conditions such as these prevail in a large part of the globe, including such regions as Florida and Southern California and even portions of the British Isles. Growing orchids on trees is not particularly difficult, but it does bring up certain problems not encountered in ordinary culture in the greenhouse or in the lath-house.

A suitable tree must be selected, for not every tree will serve. A relatively rough-barked one, such as an oak or a mango, is the best; trees such as pines, which have a flaky bark, or casuarinas ("Australian pines"), which are too densely shady, should be avoided. In addition, all coniferous trees are filled with an injurious resin which will soon exert an adverse effect on any orchid it touches.

The placing of the plant on the tree is simple. As much as possible of the potting-medium from the specimen's roots should be trimmed off (assuming that the plant has previously been grown in a pot or basket), with all obviously dead or inactive roots. Many specialists have recommended the placing of a small pad of osmunda or tree-fern fiber between the plant's base and the tree bark, but in most instances this materially slows down the attachment of the plant. The mechanical affixing of the orchid to the tree is most readily done by tapping four long, large-headed, galvanized nails into the tree, two on each side of the plant, and tightly stretching some thin galvanized wires across the roots and rhizome of the orchid. If necessary, a couple of large insulated galvanized staples may be placed astride the rhizome, but this should be done with extreme care, as this part of the plant is annoyingly brittle. For satisfactory results, the orchid plant must be tightly affixed against the surface of the tree, so that it is immovable; unless this is done, proper rooting on the new surface will be slow. Wire used for this purpose must never contain copper, for it is injurious to epiphytic plants. Nylon thread or fishing-line is occasionally used in place of wire, with excellent results; its greater pliability facilitates placement of the plant.

Since orchids are relatively slow-growing plants, it will require anywhere from several months to more than a year for the newly planted specimen on the tree to become securely attached. Orchids should be placed on trees when their new growths have matured, just before the next pseudobulb or stem, with its attendant roots, is ready to be produced. These plants on trees should, at least until they are well established, be given somewhat more water than they would normally receive in the greenhouse, since run-off and evaporation are higher than in an enclosure. With few exceptions, orchids on a tree should be placed where they will receive copious light. Some of them, such as most of the Vandas, many Cattleyas and Laelias (especially *Laelia* section *Schomburgkia*), and many of the Epidendrums, require almost full exposure to the sun in order to produce their full quota of flowers. Liberal applications of weak manure-water are highly beneficial to orchids grown on trees, particularly during the period of establishment in their new homes. The liquid is poured over the base of the plant and on its roots and foliage, or may be sprayed on through a hose-attachment. Commercial orchid fertilizers also may be used to good advantage.

What kinds of orchids may be grown on trees? A list would occupy far more space than is available here, but in general it may be stated that virtually all epiphytic types are suitable. Most Cattleyas, whether

Aerides odoratum. An especially large specimen of this lovely "Fox-Tail Orchid" grown in a private garden on the island of Jamaica.

G. C. GUNTER

species or hybrids, do well on tree trunks or branches; Dendrobiums of almost every sort thrive when tacked onto a suitably sunny tree; Epidendrums and Oncidiums and a host of the delightfully varied "botanical" orchids flourish in such impromptu aerial gardens; Vandas, which are among the most successful of all orchids cultivated in many tropical regions, grow with prodigious vigor, inching their way up the bark in a welter of healthy robust roots, and throwing their flowers in profusion, often more frequently than when confined to the green-house; even some of the hardier kinds of Phalaenopsis make admirable tree orchids in warm areas, provided they have a sufficiently moist situation.

Tree ferns of such genera as *Cyathea, Alsophila, Cibotium,* aɪ *Hemitelia* make excellent host trees for orchids because of the fiber on the trunks, which is widely used as an orchid potting-medium. The plants are readily attached to this in the manner outlined above for hard-barked trees. The porous trunks are particularly beneficial, since they retain quantities of moisture over long periods of time. Most palms, also the screw pines (*Pandanus utilis* and other members of the genus) are likewise admirably suited for the outdoor culture of epiphytic orchids.

Many orchids that oddly languish in the greenhouse or lath-house exhibit exceptional vigor when placed on trees in the garden. Here their handsome flowers add immeasurable interest to the landscape.

Growing Orchids on Rocks

A large number of orchids are found growing on rocks in their native haunts. Certain tropical species, in fact, are seldom seen on trees, but exhibit a marked predilection for the stony surfaces afforded by granite boulders, old lava flows, and rocky outcrops. In the vicinity of Rio de Janeiro, for example, the precipitous cliffs of the mountains are often heavily carpeted with orchids, of such genera as *Cattleya, Laelia, Pleurothallis, Epidendrum, Oncidium,* and a host of others. Many other types of plants grow in close conjunction with the orchids —plants such as lichens, mosses, ferns, bromeliads, gesneriads, vellozias (a group of amaryllis-like plants with woody stems), cacti, and peperomias. Around the bases of these saxicolous gardens one finds an accumulation of humus which often obscures the root-systems and rhizomes of the orchids and their neighbors. From this we infer that the detritus furnishes a certain amount of food to the plants, and also aids in the retention of moisture from rains and dews. When growing orchids on rocks, therefore, this condition should be duplicated as closely as possible. This is easily done by packing suitable humus— leaf-mould, old leaves, and even a little porous friable soil—around the bases of the plants. By careful watering for a few days, this humus will be washed down into the interstices of the rocks, where it will act as a beneficial fertilizing agent. Weak manure-water or liquid solutions of commercial orchid fertilizers may also be poured over the roots and rhizomes from time to time.

"How can I attach my orchids to a rock?" is a logical question at this juncture. Unless one of the porous, light, volcanic pumices is being used (see below for further comments on these boulders), attaching plants is not always simple, since few rocks are sufficiently soft to allow nails to be driven into them, as is possible on a tree. The best method when dealing with hard stone, such as granite (which is beloved by many orchids in the wild), is to place the bare-root orchids in any slight depression in the rock, and carefully weigh down the base of the plant with small stones or pieces of brick, taking care not to injure the new growths or expanding eyes. It may help to put a thin layer of osmunda, tree-fern fiber, or sphagnum moss under the plant until the new roots are produced; these will then grow through the moisture-retaining material and soon attach themselves to the rock's surface. If care is taken with watering, the plant may merely be laid upon the stone, and in time (but it will not be a short time!) the roots will affix it without further aid from the grower.

A great many orchids are suitable for rock-culture—virtually all of the more robust species (and indeed many that are not so notably sturdy) that are found in nature growing on trees, as well as those that are naturally lithophytic. Almost all of the Cattleyas, Laelias, pseudobulbous Epidendrums, Oncidiums, Dendrobiums, and many epiphytic groups make excellent subjects for rocks.

Various types of rocks may be used for the growing of orchidaceous plants. By far the most suitable are the now-available pumice stones (sold under several trade names), which are volcanic in origin and are mostly obtained (at least in the United States) from Hawaii or California. These extremely porous rocks, which can be cut readily with a sharp saw, are ideal for use as orchid containers in the garden (or even in the greenhouse) and are highly recommended to enterprising hobbyists. Pieces of granite are also used, though granite offers more difficulties. In general, rocks that have a high degree of alkalinity—such as common limestone, coral rock or the coquina stone of Southern Florida and other areas—should be avoided, unless they have been thoroughly leached by rainwater for several years, to remove all injurious elements.

Orchids that are grown on rocks can generally withstand more direct sunlight—once they are well established—than those cultivated in pots or baskets or even on trees. Caution should be exercised initially, however, to avoid burning of the foliage. Later the plants will become accustomed to their sunny situation. Watering must be attended to with care, of course, since the run-off is measurably greater from a rock than from the absorbent composts usually used. During the hot summer months, in particular, in addition to periodic heavy soakings, spraying of the plants on rocks is almost essential more than once each day.

Growing Orchids in Outdoor Beds

In the temperate zone as well as in the tropics, certain orchids—notably the terrestrial types but also many others—can be satisfactorily established in the ground outdoors. Those that are native in northern climes or at high altitudes—the basically hardy ones—will receive different treatment from those of more tropical origin, which are not hardy in cold regions.

Hardy orchids. There are hundreds of species of orchids suitable for outdoor cultivation in the cooler portions of the world. Elsewhere in this volume these are designated by the temperature-requirement symbol (C). Their basic cultural needs vary from genus to genus (and often within a single genus), and the reader should refer to the individual group under discussion for details. When grown in the rockery or garden, these hardy orchids need much the same conditions as those afforded more ordinary garden plants. Some of them thrive in acid soils, others demand a more alkaline or neutral condition. Proper drainage of the bed in which they are grown is most essential.

Tropical orchids. Many orchids of tropical origin are particularly adaptable to cultivation in outdoor beds. Of these we should mention the vast majority of the huge *Vanda* group with their multitudinous allied genera and hybrid groups, also *Cymbidium,* many Dendrobiums, *Epidendrum* (especially the handsome "reed-stem" species and hybrids), *Paphiopedilum, Arundina, Spathoglottis, Calanthe, Phaius, Cyrtopodium,* and others. In commercial cultivation in the Hawaiian Islands, Malaya, and elsewhere, a large percentage of the Vandas and their allies raised for cut-flower production are grown in this way. Outdoor beds simplify the cultural requirements and reduce expenditure for space under glass or lath protection when quantities of plants are being grown.

For best results, a bed should be specially constructed, raised from the surface of the ground so that drainage can be controlled. A level space is scraped in the soil, at a depth of two inches or so, and beds of the size required are built up from it. To surround the beds, hard wood of long life should be used; softer wood deteriorates too quickly through rotting and molding. Planks as much as one foot in height are often used, though the depth of the bed is largely dependent upon the whim or needs of the individual grower. It has been found, how-ever, that beds 10 to 12 inches deep are more satisfactory, since shal-lower ones will not allow for adequate compost and drainage for the roots.

Drainage in the form of broken crock or brick is then put into the frame of the bed two to three inches deep. The planting medium is filled in nearly to the top of the framework. Different growers have divergent ideas about the correct compost to use for various kinds of orchids, but in general a suitable basic medium is that described on page 52 of this book. Epiphytic orchids grown in beds such as these generally need a higher percentage of osmunda or other fibrous mate-rials in this basic formula than do the true terrestrial or semiterrestrial types.

Planting is easily accomplished by digging a hole of suitable size in the compost. The basal roots of the plants are placed in this and the medium is replaced around them. Since a porous, well ventilated medium is necessary for successful cultivation of almost all orchidaceous plants, it is advisable not to pack this compost too tightly around the roots in the beds. A heavy watering should be given the bed after planting, and no further moisture should be applied for about a week. After that, a regular watering schedule can be set up.

Since most orchids grown in beds have elongate stems, adequate staking and tying are virtual necessities. Fertilizing—with manure-water, dried sheep or cow manure, or one of the good commercial orchid fertilizers—is recommended for all orchids grown in this manner. While a rather exposed spot usually suits them well, some protection must be furnished the plants in chilly weather if they are susceptible to cold injury. Orchids grown in beds should never be planted close together, because their root-systems often become large, and overcrowding can damage their health.

Writing in the *Malayan Orchid Review* (4: 24–25. Sept. 1949), Dr. R. E. Holttum makes some pertinent comments on the cultivation of species and hybrids of *Vanda* and *Arachnis* in outdoor beds in Singa-pore:

"The slow-growing epiphytic species of *Vanda*, such as *V. tricolor* and *V. Dearei*, are usually cultivated in pots or baskets. The quicker-growing climbing species of *Arachnis* are usually grown on posts, with compost of some kind at the base to accommodate the feeding roots. Hybrids between the two are intermediate in habit and in the rate of growth. At first we grew them in pots, because as young plants this was necessary. But when they began to grow tall it seemed more convenient to put them into beds in the open ground. A trench was dug two feet wide and two feet deep, and the earth entirely removed. The trench was then filled to half its depth with old broken bricks and other similar rubble, to give good drainage: this was necessary, because the soil was a heavy clay, but in a sandy soil it would not be necessary. The rubble was then covered with half-rotted garden compost of a quantity sufficient to fill the trench level with the general surface of the ground. Two rows of posts were put into the trench, and the plants tied to the posts. Afterwards new compost, or fresh grass cuttings, or spent hops, sometimes with the addition of fresh cattle manure, were added about every three months. As soon as the plants had formed new feeding roots which grew down into the compost they began to grow strongly. The bedded plants need watering only in the driest weather [in Singapore], but potted plants must be watered every day, often twice a day."

VEGETATIVE PROPAGATION

Although the great majority of commercially grown orchids today are raised from seed, for the average amateur collector, vegetative propagation is, in most instances, an easier course to follow. Propagation by seed is, at best, a relatively difficult project for the hobbyist to undertake (see pages 74 to 81). He may augment his collection with facility by vegetative divisions, even though much less rapidly and in less large quantities than by seed.

Most orchids, such as Cattleyas, Dendrobiums, and Cymbidiums, among others, should not be divided until they have reached relatively good size, for a plant with just a few pseudobulbs or stems is never an especially strong one, and its production of flowers is naturally lessened. In most commonly grown pseudobulbous orchids, the plants should not be split up until they possess from eight to a dozen good pseudobulbs. Then they may be divided by neatly severing the rhizome with a sharp knife or pointed clippers and pulling the mass of roots which was in the container carefully apart. Most authorities recommend—with good reason—that the rhizome should be cut through one or two months before the actual mechanical division of the specimen, as this affords the two parts of the plant a better opportunity to adjust themselves, and also allows the wounded rhizome to heal thoroughly before the shock of removing part of the plant occurs.

The grower should remember that, the bigger the propagation, the more rapid will be its re-establishment as a healthy plant. With the exception of *Cymbidium* and *Dendrobium* and a few other groups, propagations of fewer than three pseudobulbs or stems should never be made. In many instances divisions ("leads" or actively growing pseudobulbs, found at the frontal part of the plant) will establish themselves so rapidly that flowers are often produced on the next season's growths. Back-bulbs, taken from the rear, and semidormant parts of the plant, often without foliage and of rather shriveled appearance, may require from three to five years for blooming. In rare or particularly valuable plants, however, especially hybrids, this is virtually the only means of propagation suitable. Hybrids may never be produced a second time from the same parents with any degree of certainty that the progeny will be duplicates of those previously obtained.

Stray solitary pseudobulbs or stems, particularly if plump and fresh in appearance, may often be induced to produce new shoots if kept immersed in water in a corner of the greenhouse, or if placed, partially buried but not so the growing eye, or bud, is covered) in moist gritty sand, or in damp sphagnum moss. They will, of course, be slow in developing to flowering size.

Offsets or offshoots (commonly referred to by their Hawaiian name of *keiki*) are plantlets produced from the upper or median parts of the stems or pseudobulbs of certain orchids, such as *Dendrobium* and *Epidendrum*. These little vegetative propagations, often produced from an abortive flower-bud, should be permitted to stay on the parent plant until they have attained some size and have three or four roots at their base. They may then be carefully severed with a sharp knife or razor blade, and potted in the manner recommended for adult plants of the same species or hybrid. These *keikis* generally produce their first flowers two to four years after removal from the parent specimen, although this period may be shortened by special attention to fertilizing and fast-growing techniques.

In some genera, notably *Phaius* and many species of *Phalaenopsis*, the old flower-spikes, after the blossoms have faded and fallen, may be cut from the plant and laid in moist sand or on dampened sphagnum moss in a warm, rather dark place. A *keiki* will generally be produced from each joint (node) of this spike, if caution is taken that it does not rot. The flower-spike may also be left on the plant, and small pads of sphagnum moss tied around the joints, but this is rather debilitating to the parent plant, and is not generally recommended.

Vegetative propagation in the monopodial orchids—such as *Vanda, Arachnis, Renanthera, Phalaenopsis, Angraecum,* and the like—is generally an annoyingly slow procedure. More and more, therefore,

Phalaenopsis hybrids. Interior of a Los Angeles greenhouse filled with these fabulous "Moth Orchids."

growers have come to rely on propagation by seed as a method of augmenting and replenishing the supply of plants of this aggregation.

Unfortunately these monopodial orchids, which basically have only a single growing tip, do not produce pseudobulbs nor thickened stems which can serve as cuttings. Seldom are *keikis* or adventitious growths produced by these monopodial orchids, and even when they do occur, they are frequently exasperatingly slow in reaching a size that warrants their removal from the parent plant. Though growing these monopodial orchids from vegetative propagations is seldom practised, in certain instances it is necessary.

In climbing genera such as *Arachnis, Renanthera,* and to a lesser degree *Vanda*, propagation by vegetative cuttings is still done with some frequency. For example, the extremely popular, floriferous and commercially important *Vanda x Miss Joaquim* is almost always increased by means of stem-cuttings. These are readily made by neatly severing the stem with a sharp cutting instrument about 15 inches from its apex; it is preferable if each cutting has two or more roots. The resultant cuttings are placed in a cool, relatively dry place for a few days, until the wound has healed, and then are rooted, generally in moist sand or damp sphagnum moss. As soon as the new roots commence to grow at or near the base of the cutting, it may be potted or planted outside in the specially prepared beds suggested for these orchids. In general, this method applies as well to the species of other genera of the monopodial orchids that have elongate stems, and it may be attempted on those plants of more abbreviated stature, though success cannot always be guaranteed.

In plants with very short stems, such as *Phalaenopsis*, a rather drastic method of vegetative propagation is often resorted to, that is, forcible removal of the apical growing tip. This is effected with a clean sharp knife; the small, still-enlarging terminal leaves should be totally cut away, along with their bases, and a small convex hollow made in the top of the plant's stem. Sulfur or other rot-inhibiting substance should be powdered on this raw wound, or rotting may occur. Usually the plant will throw off one or more subsidiary shoots at or near this mutilated apex. When they have reached a sufficiently large size these may be removed and allowed to root in the manner noted above. This method should be used with extreme caution and only when the production of seed is impractical or stem-cuttings are not available, for the plant on which this system is tried may not survive this difficult and highly debilitating operation.

BARK PREPARATIONS

Since the first days of orchid cultivation, people have experimented with a wide and often rather amazing variety of potting media in which to grow their prized specimens. At first, orchidists attempted to cultivate their plants in such strange composts as tan-bark, garden loam, and even more radically unsuitable substances.

Later, growers found that sphagnum moss and certain types of fern rhizomes and their by-products formed suitable materials for potting. And during this century, the osmunda-fern fibers and the various forms of tree-fern products have become the most widespread of all potting media for orchids.

Now, within the past few years, a new series of composts for orchids has appeared on the scene. These have virtually revolutionized the cultivation of orchids—particularly in the western United States, where the new composts were developed—and have, to a considerable degree, altered our basic concepts of orchid cultivation. These are the several bark preparations, derived from the shredded and/or chopped bark of a variety of coniferous trees, including Douglas fir, white fir, several types of pines, cedars.

The bark media are produced in several parts of this country, but primarily in the large lumbering areas of California, Oregon, and Washington. Their preparation varies somewhat from one firm to another, but consists basically of mechanically chopping or shredding the tree-bark (which has been removed from the tree during the lumbering process) into chunks of varying dimensions, and then steaming the resultant product, often under pressure, to remove the potentially injurious resins.

The bark preparations are available in several different sizes. Special, small-chopped sizes are offered as being particularly suitable for seedling orchids. Medium-size pieces are recommended for most adult orchids, while the larger pieces are suggested by the producers for Vandas and their allies.

These various sizes are available in packages or sacks of differing dimensions, ranging from small "hobby" bags to ones containing from two to three cubic feet of bark. Price naturally varies considerably, being for the most part higher on the East Coast than in the West; these bark preparations are, however, still considerably more reasonable in cost than osmunda or tree-fern fiber.

Almost all of these products, when delivered, contain small fibers and dust. For best results in using bark preparations these particles should be removed, by sifting them through a coarse- or fine-mesh screen; otherwise, when potting, the particles tend to pack together, thus obstructing the perfect drainage which is essential to all orchids.

Many orchid growers, both amateur and professional, have within the past year or two transferred all of their plants to one or another of these composts. Many experts have been put on record as stating that bark preparations are the final answer to the potting problems of all orchidaceous plants, while other authorities are somewhat more reserved in their enthusiasm. It does seem evident—as shall be pointed out later—that not all types of orchids thrive in these composts, as was initially supposed.

The extraordinary ease with which the bark preparations may be used in potting is among their most important attributes. In using osmunda or tree-fern fiber, for example, several minutes' time is required to pot a single average plant; in the same period, upwards of six or eight plants may be potted when utilizing the various bark composts.

When an already established plant is being moved from osmunda into bark, two procedures are suggested: either the careful removal of all the old compost from around the roots of the orchid (this is most commonly done), or a ball of roots and old osmunda—provided it is not overly stale or rotting—retained on the plant, all excess old materials being removed. The latter system naturally gives greater ease in keeping the plant firmly in the pot when the bark is added around it.

The same sort of pots should be used for these composts as for osmunda or tree-fern fiber, and they should be filled one-third to one-half with broken crock or cracked brick. The bark preparation should be moistened several hours in advance of its use, to facilitate potting. In most areas—particularly in such rainy spots as South Florida and many tropical lands—it should be mixed with about equal parts of chopped tree-fern fiber, or chunks of tree-fern, to facilitate rapid drainage.

The orchid plant is set into the pot, and the damp bark gradually poured or handed in around its roots. The compost should be tamped down from time to time with the thumbs or the blunt end of a potting-stick, and the pot filled to within about one-half inch of its rim; after watering, a certain amount of settling will occur, thus lowering the level of the compost still further.

Galvanized wire staples may be used to pin the orchid to the compost. If the plant seems top-heavy, stakes and tie-strings may be added.

To thoroughly soak the new compost, the plant, in its pot, should be plunged into a bucket of water. The compost may then be packed down more thoroughly, and the plant will remain in place more securely.

The bark preparations are particularly useful for newly imported plants, because they encourage rapid formation of rampant root-systems, much more so than do osmunda or tree-fern fiber. Back-bulbs also seem to commence growth more rapidly in these composts, and sick or injured specimens make a hasty recovery in bark, often accomplishing in a few months what might require a year or more in other composts.

Certain delicate and refractory orchids, which in general do not do well in osmunda or any of the other commonly used composts, often thrive when potted in bark. Many types of *Pleurothallis* and allied genera, for example, are far more successful in these new media than in the old osmunda. Monopodial orchids, such as Vandas and Angraecums, which have been injured so that the growing apex has ceased production, will rapidly regain their vigor, and produce offshoots and new roots with satisfying rapidity.

Because of the thorough drainage afforded by these bark preparations, more water is required than in other composts. When first potted, the plants should be examined after every watering, to be certain that they are still firmly in place in their containers. It is suggested, when watering these composts, that a "water-breaker" be used, rather than the strong stream from a hose-nozzle, which may sluice the plant out of the pot.

Under glass, the bark media sometimes tend to become overly wet and almost soggy. This condition should be watched for and avoided, or the health of the plants will be seriously impaired. The addition of the previously suggested chopped (or chunk) tree-fern in most cases readily corrects the trouble. It would also be noted that the majority of the bark preparations made up of pine and/or cedar bark seem to deteriorate under average conditions so rapidly that the compost must be replenished every six months or so, hence we definitely do not recommend their use by the orchidist.

As a whole, these bark preparations seem to be deficient in nitrogen; therefore, regular applications of a fertilizer with high nitrogen-content is suggested. Granted that fertilizing causes somewhat more rapid deterioration of the bark preparations, the results in plant growth warrant its use.

Some experts state that the new bark media are not the "cure-all" mixtures they are claimed to be. In some collections, for example, flowers of such genera as *Cattleya*, *Laelia*, and even the Dendrobiums of the *D. bigibbum* var. *Phalaenopsis* aggregation do not last in good condition for as long as normal, when potted in these modern composts. This is perhaps due to other factors, but further research may prove that these orchids, and certain others, should not be potted in bark preparations.

For example, in my own collection, I have removed all of the Cattleyas and allied genera from the bark preparations and mixtures thereof, and have repotted them in straight osmunda fiber, finding that under my particular conditions they do markedly better. A few other plants that have come under observation—including certain "reed-type" Epidendrums and some kinds of *Elleanthus*—have rapidly deteriorated in bark.

As yet, we really do not know enough about the vagaries of these relatively new bark preparations to make sweeping statements concerning their use. Their effect on the thousands of different kinds of orchids now in cultivation is a matter for further research.

ORCHID AILMENTS

Orchids, like all other kinds of plants, are occasionally afflicted with a rather wide variety of pests and diseases, the great majority of which are easily controlled. Clean, pest-free plants are of course essential to the success of a collection, no matter how large or small it may be. A diseased or insect-ridden specimen often may not produce sufficiently strong growths to flower, and thus the entire purpose of having orchid plants is defeated.

The first thing about the plant's health to be noted by the novice in orchid-growing is the actual culture afforded them in the greenhouse, lath-house, or home. In general the plants should *never* be grown "soft" (that is, with insufficient light, so that their growths become spindly, pale or yellow-green, and rather loose in habit), but rather more on the "hard" side (that is, with more light, so that the growths become sturdy, dark green, and firm in texture). "Soft"-grown orchids are in almost all cases much more susceptible to attack by insects or diseases than those grown in the stronger and more normal "hard" way.

Pests of Orchids. We should first, in this discussion of orchid ailments, consider the pests—noxious insects and the like. These are basically of two sorts, the biting ones and the sucking ones. In the initial category we find ants, weevils, Cattleya fly, cockroaches, palmetto bugs, springtails, sowbugs, slugs, and snails. Not only do most of these pests attack the vegetative parts of the plant—pseudobulbs or stems and foliage—but some of them frequently cause serious damage to the buds or expanding flowers, generally rendering them unsightly and useless. These pests may be controlled by use of a good stomach poison, which is generally mixed with water and sprayed on the plants, on which it leaves a residual film. Among the best of the wide variety of stomach poisons currently available are the various DDT dusts, tetra-ethyl-pyrophosphate (TEPP—Vapotone), arsenic salts in dust form, metaldehyde, and Chlordane.

The sucking pests, such as scale, thrips, mealy bugs, aphids, and red-spider mites, are often found on orchids brought in from the wild, and with inattention may become firmly entrenched in the collection. A contact spray on the plants should be used to combat these annoying and destructive pests. Excellent for this purpose are nicotine sulphate (Black Leaf 40), DDT spray or emulsion (DeeDeeTox), pyrethrum in its several available forms, rotenone, Chlordane, lime sulphur, and benzene hexachloride (Lindane, BHC). The DDT preparations are generally considered the most efficient today for the average small collection, and are the most widely used for this purpose.

Two very poisonous substances, Malathion and Parathion, are used by some orchidists. Although extremely efficient in ridding the collection of all pests, we do not advocate their use by the novice, because they can prove fatal to the user. Such extreme caution must be taken in their application that they should be handled only by an expert.

Of all the pests noted here, scale insects are probably the most annoying to and prevalent with the orchid grower. These may be removed manually from an infested plant by scrubbing with a soft brush dipped in warm soapy water, with particular care being taken to reach all the hidden parts of the plant, such as the inside of the leaf-sheaths, the joints of the rhizome, etc. Scale can also be controlled with some effectiveness by a regular spraying with 5% DDT or Lindane.

Orchid Diseases. Diseases of orchids, whether caused by bacteria, viruses, or fungi, are seldom encountered today, and as a consequence are not too well known. Many diseased plants are not recognized as such, and an orchid afflicted with some ailment of this sort may continue to live and flower for years without noticeable deterioration, either vegetatively or in its production of blossoms. Conversely, however, not only may the afflicted plant suddenly fail and die, but also it may spread its disease to plants growing nearby, with fatal results. Therefore, the control of disease—and especially the segregation of plants already infected—is a very important phase of this problem.

Diseases may be partly prevented by careful growing methods, the most important of which is the watering of plants only during the morning hours, so that by afternoon—when natural humidity in the air is higher and temperatures are usually more favorable to the growth and spread of fungus spores and bacteria—they will have dried out and a relatively inhospitable situation is presented to the disease-causing agents. Overcrowding of plants in the collection (especially in the enclosed greenhouse) should also be avoided, since with the decreased circulation of air the heavily moisture-laden plants do not dry out as much as is necessary.

Sprays and contact poisons naturally do not have any effect on a diseased plant, though sprays at least may be used as a partially preventive measure and may combat the ailment in its earliest stages. Often it is necessary to cut off the diseased portion of the plant; this diseased part should be burned at once, and never allowed to remain in the vicinity of other plants, even for a short period of time. Fungicidal sprays may be used to prevent spread of disease. In an infected house humidity and watering should be decreased, and ventilation greatly increased, until the disease is eliminated.

All diseased parts of a plant should be carefully cut out with a clean knife, and the wound should then be covered with a film of Bordeaux paste, which is available from most orchid supply houses. Caution should be exercised to sterilize any knives or other implements that have touched the diseased plant, by soaking in alcohol or a commercial disinfectant. The grower should also wash his hands thoroughly after touching a diseased plant and before handling other plants.

Although diseases of orchids do not occur frequently, the beginning hobbyist should be aware that they do exist, and that their control is possible, with adequate care and attention. The procedures for keeping orchid plants healthy are sensible and simple.

SOWING OF SEED

Today, as a result of tremendous advances made in the field, the vast majority of orchid propagations are made by seed, rather than by the vegetative methods outlined elsewhere in this book (see pages 64 to

Gardeners' Chronicle

Left, seed capsule of *Peristeria pendula* after dehiscence.
Right, seed capsule of *Odontoglossum maxillare*.

67). Not only does this apply, of necessity, to the thousands of artificial (and natural) hybrids now known, but also to certain rare or particularly desirable species and forms of species not otherwise obtainable in quantity.

The growing of orchids from seed, while not a prohibitively difficult

task, is still not a simple one. Many amateur orchidists have so perfected the involved techniques of the process, however, that it has become "second nature" to them. But these enthusiasts succeed only by paying

Vanda x Alice Fukunaga. Note the seed capsule near the right-hand lower-leaf of this plant.

explicit attention to all of the innumerable details presented by the process, plus exerting considerable patience and great caution in the actual mechanics of the operation, from its initiation to its completion.

The seeds of orchids, which are produced by the hundreds of thousands, or even millions) in each capsule, are highly fragile structures, possessed of virtually no stored food materials, or endosperm, such as most other seeds contain. They consist merely of a minute oval or roundish proembryo, surrounded by an incredibly intricate sheath of branched, interlocking fibers; these fibers break down and are apparently used, at least in part, by the developing proembryo shortly after germination, thus furnishing some infinitesimal quantity of nutriment. The person attempting to grow these plants from seed, therefore, must not only protect the tiny seeds from injury and infestation by noxious pests and fungi, to which they are particularly susceptible, but must also furnish the germinating proembryos with food materials, that they may continue to grow. In nature, this food is supplied by an endophytic fungus, the minute multicellular branches of which (called *hyphae*) actually penetrate the proembryo of the orchid seed and furnish both carbohydrates for food and a state of acidity sufficient for germination. The relationship of the endophytic fungus with the seed is called *symbiosis*, and the fungusless method used in seed culture today is termed *asymbiotic*, because of the absence of this symbiotic endophytic fungus.

Under the asymbiotic system, which will be discussed here (see page 80 for comments on the symbiotic method of growing orchid seed), the seeds are sown on various sterilized media—generally agar jelly, which is produced from a seaweed. To this, certain necessary nutrients, both organic and inorganic, have been added and adjusted to a suitable stage of acidity.

The Asymbiotic Method

Once the orchid seeds have been obtained, they should be sown as soon as possible, since the very small available food supply does not make them a particularly favorable subject for protracted storage, and their proportionate viability decreases at an alarming rate. The best place to accomplish this delicate process of sowing the orchid seed is in a relatively small, clean room, where there is a minimum of moving air and as little dust as possible. Since one of the primary objectives of asymbiotic culture is to avoid the introduction of bacteria and fungal spores into the planting medium, it is recommended that the grower tie a surgical mask or clean, freshly boiled handkerchief over his nose and mouth, and carefully use a mild germicide to rinse his hands and lower arms, as well as the outside of the flasks or tubes and instruments to be used. It is also wise to spray the air over the table or bench on which the seed-sowing is to be done with water from an atomizer, as this aids in settling any dust in the area.

Before these last-minute precautions have been taken, however, the orchidist must have prepared his flasks, bottles, or tubes for the reception of the seeds. One of two basic formulae (Knudson "B" or "C") is generally adopted by modern growers, on the grounds that these are the most suitable, nutritionally, for the seedlings, and the easiest to make up. For the beginning orchid grower—and, indeed, for almost all except those persons who expect to sow seeds in large quantities—it is not recommended that these exacting and complex formulae[1] be made up in the home, but rather that they be purchased already mixed with the agar jelly, from commercial establishments that specialize in their preparation. These mixed formulae, with the agar, are also available at very moderate prices already prepared in the flasks or tubes, so that the seeds may be sown directly on these media without the attendant difficulties of preparation which are so deliberate and time-consuming.

Instructions are furnished by the manufacturers with these prepared agar-nutrient mixtures and also with the filled flasks. However, a few steps are necessary before the actual sowing of the seeds. These are the sterilization of the planting-medium and of the seed itself, which has almost certainly become contaminated by bacteria or fungal spores since it was removed from the ripened capsule.

The prepared flasks are placed in an autoclave (or pressure cooker) for a sterilization period of about 20 minutes, at 15 pounds pressure. The hot flasks should then be removed and placed on their sides, with the aperture of each somewhat propped upward, so that a large, even

---

[1] The following is Knudson's Formula "C," now the most frequently used of the pair, given here for the orchidist who wishes to experiment by himself.

calcium nitrate	$Ca(NO_3)_2 \cdot 4H_2O$	1.00	gram
monobasic potassium phosphate	KH_2PO_4	0.25	gram
magnesium sulfate	$MgSO_4 \cdot 7H_2O$	0.25	gram
ammonium sulfate	$(NH_4)_2SO_4$	0.50	gram
sucrose	$C_{12}H_{22}O_{11}$	20.00	grams
ferrous sulfate	$FeSO_4 \cdot 7H_2O$	0.025	gram
manganese sulfate	$MnSO_4 \cdot 4H_2O$	0.0075	gram

Add the above ingredients, one at a time, to one liter (1000 cc.) of distilled water, and dissolve completely. Fifteen grams of agar is then added, and the mixture warmed in a double boiler until all of the agar has dissolved. The pH must then be checked very accurately, and adjusted to that required by the particular seed being sown. Most orchid seeds grow best in a solution having a pH of 5.0 to 5.2.

surface of the medium will be presented for sowing of the seed when the agar-nutrient mixture hardens. Flasks (or tubes) kept in this horizontal position offer less opportunity for contamination during the actual sowing of the seed, as well as for contamination later on. As soon as the flasks have thoroughly cooled and the medium within them has solidified, actual sowing of the seed may begin.

Meanwhile, the seed itself is sterilized by immersion in a solution of commercial bleaching powder (calcium hypochlorite, or chloride of lime), which may also be purchased in a prepared state from concerns furnishing the mixed agar-nutrient medium. Ten grams of the bleaching powder are mixed thoroughly with 140 cc. of distilled water, and the solution is allowed to settle; after filtering, the clear solution should be used at once. (Stale sterilizing solution should be discarded, as it loses its potency from day to day.) The seeds are then placed in a small test-tube and approximately five times as much of the sterilizing agent as seeds added; the seeds are left in the tube for about 15 to 20 minutes, and they should be shaken sharply several times during this sterilizing period. The seeds are removed to the prepared, sterilized flasks directly from this germicidal tube.

Seeds are most easily removed and placed upon the culture medium by means of a small "inoculating needle," which can be made from a strand of platinum wire. A tiny loop bent at one end of this needle serves as a sort of spoon, and a loopful of sterilized seeds is easily moved to the damp surface of the agar-nutrient medium in the flask or bottle. After each inoculation the needle should be sterilized, by heating it to red heat over a gas or alcohol flame, then allowed to cool. The seeds, once placed in the flask, should be spread evenly over the surface of the medium by careful rotation of the container. The amateur should be particularly careful not to sow too much seed in the flask, for overcrowded seedlings are never healthy ones. For a 500 cc. flask, for example, not more than 400 seedlings (preferably somewhat fewer) should be permitted, or else difficulties and unhealthy growth will ensue. The apex and neck of the seeded flask is then rotated in a gas or alcohol flame, the stopper (which has also been put through the flame) is pushed in securely, and the prepared flask is set at its proper angle, with the surface of the agar as nearly horizontal as possible— and the job is finished.

Certain precautions must be taken after the sowing of the seed, to prevent the increase and growth of the contaminating bacteria and fungi which are still present in and around the prepared flask. The best method of avoiding this late contamination is by swabbing the neck of the sown flask with a saturated solution of copper sulfate, obtainable in drug stores as bluestone; the upper half of the cotton plug used as a stopper should also be soaked in this solution. Bichloride of mercury may be used as a substitute disinfectant. Heavy waxed paper, soaked in the solution, should be tied with strong string or a rubber band to cover the cotton stopper and neck of the flask.

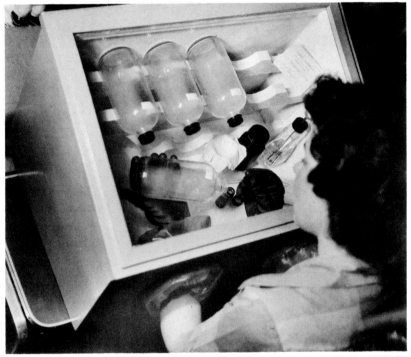

DANIEL RYERSON

A special case for the flasking of orchid seed.

Most orchid seed germinates best if kept at temperatures of 70–75° F., in a relatively shaded, moist spot. A greenhouse shelf is often very acceptable for this purpose. Many contemporary growers keep their seed-flasks on specially built shelves in the house, but often the excessive dryness of the atmosphere will exert a deleterious effect on the agar-nutrient mixture and on the germinating seedlings. Recent experiments have shown that by giving the young seedlings added light—by means of fluorescent lamps, left burning at night—growth is noticeably quickened.

Tubes or flasks containing already germinated seedlings, often of fine and valuable orchids, are now available from many sources at low prices. These contain several hundred well-established seedlings, generally almost ready for transplanting into community pots. They are highly recommended for the orchidist who wishes to experiment with young seedlings, but does not wish to bother with actually sowing his own seed and waiting the requisite period for them to reach the size for transplanting from the flask stage. With such species and hybrids as those of the *Vanda* group, which are often of exasperatingly slow growth in their juvenile stages, these flasks of established seedlings are particularly worth while.

Two Earlier Methods

An alternate method or two of raising orchid seedlings have long been known, but these have now largely gone out of vogue, despite their ready adaptability to the needs of the amateur hobbyist. They involve the use either of host orchids or of specially prepared beds. In the early days of orchid breeding, all seedlings were raised by these methods, and since they do away with the necessity of careful preparation of the agar-nutrient medium and the attention that must be paid to sterile conditions, they can be heartily recommended for the small collector who wishes to raise but a few seedlings. Germination by this means is often rather low, only about 10% of the possible total, as compared with as much as 80–90% when the asymbiotic method is used, but it still may be sufficient for the amateur.

Here again, for best results, seed should be sown as soon as gathered. If a host plant is used, it is not essential that it be of the same species as the seeds being sown, although there is some evidence that better germination results if this is done, because of the identity of the endophytic fungi present. Many growers suggest that a special top-dressing of fresh, actively growing sphagnum moss be added to the compost around the host plant; if this can be done several months before sowing, results often seem markedly improved. The mechanics of actual sowing are singularly simple in this case: the seed (which is not sterilized, as in the asymbiotic system) is merely sprinkled evenly over the surface of the compost around the host, and lightly sprayed with water. The mature specimen, around which the sowing of the seed has been done, is then treated as usual, the only care necessary being in watering, to avoid flushing out the minute seeds. Excessive exposure to sunlight should be avoided during the germination period, or the tiny seedlings may become burned or grow with trying slowness.

Other authorities suggest the preparation of special seed beds. These may either be pots or, preferably, flat pottery pans about four inches in diameter. They should be thoroughly cleaned and filled about half full with broken crock or brick, to facilitate drainage, which is extremely important for the plantlets. Various composts are used, but the best one appears to be a mixture of equal parts of finely chopped brown osmunda fiber and finely chopped fresh sphagnum moss. This medium is added to the pan or pot to within about three-quarters of an inch of the rim, and the surface trimmed neatly. A piece of old linen or canvas, which has previously been boiled for thirty minutes or so, is then spread over the pot, and its edges pressed in around the inner rim, in such a way that the surface is smooth and the center slightly raised. Some orchidists then add a top-dressing of fresh green sphagnum moss, but this does not seem essential for success. Sowing is done as in the case of the host plants noted above. A sheet of glass covers the entire apparatus, and aids in retention of moisture and warmth, as well as protecting the seedlings from pests such as slugs, snails, and cockroaches. This glass should, for best effect, be lightly painted or fixed with a sheet of shading tissue paper, so that the small plants will not suffer from burning by sunlight. Watering must be done cautiously, with a fine spray-nozzle or syringe. If the beds dry out too much, they may be partly dipped in water, permitting the moisture to seep through to the surface. Extremes of wetness or dryness, which are to be avoided, can only be obviated by daily inspection, coupled with the careful use of the water-sprayer.

After eight weeks or so (dependent largely upon the type of orchid being grown), the tiny green globules (called *protocorms*) usually commence to appear. When the first little leaves are visible, the seedlings may be transplanted into community pots and treated as mentioned in the section of this work devoted to the cultivation of juvenile plants (pages 82 to 86). The seed beds should be retained, undisturbed, for several months, as other seedlings will appear at different times.

SEEDLINGS AND THEIR CARE

Orchid seedlings are ready for transplanting from the flasks, tubes or bottles in which they were started (or from around the host-plants or specially prepared beds, if those were used), at various times, depending entirely upon the species or hybrid involved. Generally,

JACK BRANT, JR.

Rows of flasks containing young-germinated orchid seedlings and ranks of community pots containing hundreds of older seedlings in a Florida collection.

when the plantlets are about one-quarter to one-half inch in height, with several of their diminutive leaves already expanded, they may be taken out and put into pots with safety; this state varies with the type of orchid involved, and may be as long as two or three years from seed (in certain of the *Vanda* group, for example), although it is generally somewhat less.

Potting of seedlings is rather similar to that of the adult plants of the particular kind of orchid concerned, although, naturally, much smaller containers and quantities of materials are used. Most seedlings should be transferred from the flask to community pots at first; then as they increase in size and vigor, to small individual thumb-pots. A wide variety of composts for seedlings at this community-pot stage has been suggested by different authorities, but the majority of contemporary experts now use a mixture made up of about equal parts of finely chopped tree-fern fiber, chopped sphagnum moss, and crushed bark preparation that is entirely dust-free. Some growers add small amounts of turkey grit or very fine vermiculite.

New, clean pots (or carefully scrubbed and scoured ones), ranging from 2½ to 4 inches in diameter, should be used for community planting of seedlings taken from the flask, each community pot to hold an average of about 30 little plants. These pots are first soaked in tap-water for several hours, then filled about one-half full with a cracked crock or other drainage materials. The remainder of the pot is then filled with the previously prepared compost. This should be rather tightly packed in, and watered with a syringe; planting in a moistened compost is much easier than if a dry medium is used. The top surface of this compost should be carefully trimmed, so that a smooth plane is presented. Small holes may then be punched to receive the roots of the transplants.

From Flask to Community Pot

The seedlings are best removed from the germinating flask or bottle by means of a long-handled spoon (such as an iced-tea spoon or bar spoon), along with a small amount of the adhering agar jelly, which will deteriorate with the passing of time and will do less harm to the fragile roots of the seedling than would its removal. Naturally these seedlings will vary considerably in size when taken from the flask. The largest ones may be handled with some ease, by placing them on top of the compost in the pot, and carefully pressing the tiny roots into the holes that have been punched in the surface of the potting-medium. Many growers use a match stick or a small metal pick (such as that favored by dentists) when potting. The smallest seedlings are best handled with forceps, the ends of which should be swathed in soft gauze or cotton, to avoid injury to the brittle little leaves; these tiny seedlings are usually just set into the crevices of the compost, which is then slightly pressed in around their bases. In time their roots should take hold.

Once filled with seedlings, the community pots should be carefully sprayed with water, and removed to their permanent location in the greenhouse. A special glass case (such as a Wardian case or "indoor greenhouse," as illustrated on page 45 is often used for cultivation of young seedlings. This may either be purchased ready-made or constructed with but little effort and expense. The greenhouse in which these juvenile orchids are grown should be kept at a relatively constant day-and-night temperature, never below 65° F., and preferably never above 80° F. Watering of such seedlings is extremely important, one of the most essential rules being that they must never be watered so late in the day that they stay wet during the night. Otherwise the inroads of bacterial rot may soon appear. On sunny warm days they may be sprayed from overhead two or three times a day, but this should always be done sufficiently early in the day so that they have a chance to dry out before dusk. In general, seedlings in the community pot stage should be watered daily, and during the hot summer months, the amount of water supplied may be increased still more, as necessary.

If possible, seedlings should be removed from their flasks during the spring months, to allow for a full summer's growth before the often semi-dormant period of fall and winter sets in. Seedlings should never be permitted to remain in the flask until they are so large that they are crowding each other, as permanent injury may result. Only the hardiest, most vigorous seedlings should be retained and potted from a flask. Weak or excessively small plantlets take much longer to reach maturity than their more robust brethren, are more susceptible to disease and mechanical injuries, and often do not develop into good specimens. Many writers have said that these "weaklings" frequently produce the finest flowers out of a given group of seedlings, but critical examination of entire sets of seedlings grown on to the blossom-stage has never proved this to be a valid claim.

The Third Move

After a period of six months to a year (or more, in certain slow-growing orchids), the seedlings in their community pots are generally ready for transplanting again, this time four or five of them into a 2½ inch pot, in exactly the same fashion as noted above. More freely moving air and available light, with slightly less overhead syringing, are suggested for the plants in this tertiary stage of their growth.

Following a comparable period of growth (during which regular fertilizing with weakened solutions is strongly recommended), these seedlings are again ready for repotting, this time into individual thumb-pots, about 1 inch in diameter. The seedlings to be transplanted should be taken out with as much of the original compost as possible intact on their roots, and this should be incorporated into the new compost, provided, of course, that it is still in fresh condition. Overpotting should always be avoided when dealing with orchids, and especially when working with seedlings; it is far better to repot the little plants frequently than to invite the difficulties of stale or soured compost which often present themselves in an overly large container. Seedlings should at all times be kept clean of scale, insect pests, and other invaders, and it is often a good practice to include them in the regular spraying routine which covers the entire collection of plants. As a rule, until seedlings reach about the individual 1-inch-pot stage of life, they should be given only about one-half as much sun and exposure as the adult plants of the same species or hybrid. Many seedlings are particularly susceptible to burning through excessive exposure, and in extreme cases this may result in their death.

The Two-inch Pot Stage

The next move is into 2-inch pots, and many orchidists have found that, at this stage, such types as *Vanda*, *Phalaenopsis*, and their allies, as well as myriad multigeneric hybrids (even Cattleyas, Oncidiums, and Dendrobiums), thrive with astounding vigor in small individual cubes or baskets made of soft wood slats or pieces of tree-fern fiber. Such containers may be bought from commercial establishments in the United States, the Hawaiian Islands, and elsewhere, or the wooden ones may readily be manufactured at home. Most orchid seedlings, particularly when they have reached this larger individually-potted stage, benefit materially by regular feeding, with fertilizers such as those noted on page 42, though the solutions should naturally be in somewhat weaker concentrations.

Orchid seedlings are not, despite the opinions of many amateurs, difficult to grow. Their cultural wants are, in the main, similar to those required by mature specimens of the same (or allied) species or hybrids, and any variations from the norm may easily be met in even the smallest collection. They are, in fact, ideally suited to the beginning (or, more advanced, for that matter) orchidist who wishes to augment his collection with rare or unusual orchids, but does not wish to pay the prices for adult specimens. A tremendous variety of orchid seedlings is now available on the market, both in the United States and abroad, and the hobbyist would do well to examine all lists of such offerings as they come to hand.

TREATMENT OF NEWLY IMPORTED ORCHIDS

Although the practice is not so common now as in the past, orchidists today, particularly in the United States, continue to import plants from the wild. Formerly, this was almost the only way to acquire orchids, but with the tremendous increase in the popularity of these plants and their more extensive commercial cultivation, they are now available in most parts of the country, readily and in general inexpensively.

All orchids—and many other plants—entering this country from abroad (except those from certified nurseries, which have been inspected and passed as clean and disease-free by agricultural authorities) are subjected to fumigation at the U.S. Department of Agriculture Plant Inspection Station nearest their point of entry. This fumigation (conducted after a thorough, careful inspection of the plants by the entomologists and pathologists of the Station) is usually a rigorous jolt to the plants, since they are placed in a sealed chamber and fumigated—generally with methyl bromide gas—under high pressure for two hours or more. The customary mortality rate for many delicate orchids so treated is discouragingly high, but it is only in this manner that such plants may be imported.

When plants are received from the fumigation station, repacked in their original cartons or containers, the following procedure should be carried out:

(1) As soon as the plants arrive, they should be carefully removed from the containers. The orchid plants are then spread out in a well-shaded, airy spot, preferably out-of-doors, so that they do not overlap one another; if open wire or lath benches are available, these are perfect for the purpose of aeration, which is most important as part of these initial preparations. Any spot that allows the just-fumigated orchids to receive a large amount of fresh, freely moving air will be suitable, but they should not be crammed into any sort of confined spot. The plants should be turned over at intervals, so that the gases residual from the gas-chamber may be fully dispelled by the breezes. These gases are lethal to the orchid specimens, hence it is most important that they be driven off as rapidly as possible.

(2) The next day the plants should be given a heavy washing with tap water, either by immersion in a large pail (this is preferred), or by very thorough soaking with a garden hose. When the pail-soaking method is used, two cups or so of ordinary household sugar (or honey) may be added to the water, and the plants allowed to stand in it for five minutes or so. This high concentration of readily-available sugars seems to give the debilitated plants a much-needed boost, and in most instances speeds their recovery from the shock of the long trip plus the fumigation. Following this washing—which must be thorough—the plants should then be spread out once more, still in the shade, and allowed to drain.

(3) If the collector can be patient for this length of time (and this is often rather difficult!), potting of the new imports should not be done until about one week or more after their arrival. Certain experts recommend the immediate potting of newly arrived specimens, but I have found that this often causes excessive rot and loss, evidently because not all of the noxious gases have managed to free themselves from the roots and rhizomes. The plants to be potted are carefully trimmed of all dead or decaying parts—with all cut surfaces dusted with flowers of sulfur or one of the new rot-inhibiting substances—and labels are made for each specimen.

With most orchids, division of large specimens into smallish clumps should be made, since this generally accelerates the production of new roots and eventual growths. There is no reason to leave old, shriveled or almost dead pseudobulbs or stems on a plant. It seems, rather, to start better if such defunct portions are carefully removed before potting.

Since newly imported plants are likely to have no live roots, a special "establishing" procedure is strongly recommended. The new arrivals should be placed in proportionately small pots, in a compost which induces rapid root-production, though it may not necessarily be the compost in which the plants will later be kept. For this purpose, under most conditions, a mixture of chopped tree-fern fiber (or small chunks of tree-fern), with an equal amount of one of the new bark preparations, plus a smaller quantity of chopped sphagnum moss, is most acceptable. This is packed as firmly as possible around the remaining roots of the plant, and if necessary (as it usually is) a staple or two, made from a length of galvanized wire, may be placed over the rhizome and pushed well down into the potting medium, to hold the plant firmly in position. For tall or top-heavy specimens, it is often helpful to use a galvanized tie-stake, with twine or plastic-covered wire to maintain the plant in an upright position. The label is put into the pot, or affixed to the plant, and the potted orchid is then ready to go outside to the greenhouse or lath-house.

(4) Immediately after potting, the compost and all parts of the plant should be thoroughly soaked, so that water runs copiously from the container for some time after. A drying-out period of about one week should then be afforded, in the case of most orchids, during which only a slight spraying should be given at frequent enough intervals to avoid undue shriveling of the plant. At the end of this week, regular watering should begin. Within a few weeks, new green-tipped roots generally appear, and in many instances, growths begin to show.

When I fertilize my orchid collection, which I do about every two weeks, I include these newly imported plants in this fertilizing schedule, provided at least one week has elapsed after their initial potting and thorough watering. Such new plants should be kept in a semi-shaded spot until root-action is rather advanced; this usually requires at least two or three months. They may then be moved to their presumed permanent situation in the collection.

(5) At the end of six to eight months (in most cases), the new imports are ready for transplanting into larger pots and, if necessary, to a different types of compost and/or container. Many orchids grow well in the basic mixture noted in section 3 above. Such types may not need transferral until they have outgrown their container or the potting medium has become exhausted. Many others, though, need to be removed at this stage from their small "establishing" pots into other containers, or into other composts for best all-round results.

For example, many orchids do better on tree-fern slabs or rafts, once they have become well established and rooted. I find, however, that when newly imported orchids are placed directly on such slabs or rafts —without adequate root-systems—they generally require many months to become established, and often do not do especially well for years to come. The system of growing new imports at first in "establishing" pots, is therefore strongly recommended for those orchids in particular.

III

The Principal Cultivated Orchids

A BEGINNER'S LIST OF EASILY
GROWN ORCHIDS

The following list of orchids—species and hybrids—suitable for cultivation by the amateur hobbyist is by no means a complete one, for in actuality almost all orchids are excellent subjects for the beginner's collection. Those named here represent only a small proportion of the types that are generally available at a relatively reasonable cost per plant.

Mature orchid plants can be purchased at any time of the year. They are shipped by the large firms suitably packaged to withstand the rigors of travel, and usually reach the collector in excellent condition. For the beginner, it is recommended that at first only adult plants be acquired, since their cultural requirements are generally less specialized than those of the often vaguely delicate seedlings. In the pseudobulbous types (those listed below in Section I), a plant should usually have at least three to five pseudobulbs when purchased; a smaller one may prove to be weak and difficult to manage. In the monopodial species (Section II below), which contain those orchids without pseudobulbs but with a leafy stem growing indefinitely upward, suitable plants ideally should have at least three pairs of leaves on the stem.

For assistance to the amateur, the orchids listed below are designated by letters signifying their temperature preference (as used throughout this volume), whether C (cool), I (intermediate), or H (hot or warm). When a species or hybrid will thrive under more than one temperature category, both (or all three) designating letters are affixed. Ideal temperature ranges are discussed on page 40 of this book.

Orchids that are particularly well suited to cultivation in the home, as house plants, are designated by an asterisk (*).

Section I. Pseudobulbous Types
(Including those with stemlike pseudobulbs or other variations).

Aspasia epidendroides (I); *A. principissa* (I)

Bifrenaria Harrisoniae (I,H)

**Bletia purpurea* (I); **B. Shepherdii* (I,H)

**Bletilla striata* and fma. *alba* (C,I)

**Brassavola cucullata* (I,H); **B. nodosa* (I,H)

**Brassia caudata* (I,H); **B. Gireoudiana* (I,H); **B. verrucosa* (I,H)

**Brassocattleya* x *Heatonensis* (I); **BC.* x *Mrs. J.H. Leeman* (I); **BC.* x *Mme. C. Maron* (I)

Bulbophyllum barbigerum (H); **B. Careyanum* (I,H); **B. Lobbii* (I,H); **B. Medusae* (I,H); **B. Pechei* (I)

**Calanthe* x *Baron Schroeder* (C,I); *C.* x *Hennisii* (I); *C. veratrifolia* (I,H); **C. vestita* (C,I,H)

Catasetum fimbriatum (I,H); **C. Oerstedii* (I,H); **C. Russellianum* (I,H); **C. viridiflavum* (I,H)

Cattleya Bowringiana* (I,H); **C.* x *Ella Mae Sutton* (I); **C.* x *Enid* (I);C.* x *Fabia* (I); *C* x *Hardyana* (I,H); **C.* x *Harold* (I); **C. labiata* (I,H) and its vars. **Gaskelliana* (I), *Lueddemanniana* (I), **Mossiae* (I), **Percivaliana* (I), **Trianaei* (I), *Warneri* (I,H), and *Warscewiczii* (I,H); *C. guttata* (I,H); **C. intermedia* (I,H); **C.* x *Octave Doin* (1); **C.* x *Peetersii* (I); **C.* x *Priscilla* and var. **alba* (I)

Chysis bractescens (I,H)

Coelogyne corymbosa (C,I); **C. cristata* (C,I); **C. Huettneriana* (C,I,H); *C. pandurata* (H)

**Cycnoches ventricosum* (I) and var. **Warscewiczii* (I,H)

Cymbidium eburneum (C,I); **C. Finlaysonianum* (I,H); **C. Lowianum* (I); **C.* x *Pauwelsii* (C,I); **C.* x *Swallow* (C,I); *C. Tracyanum* (C,I)

Cyrtopodium Andersoni (I,H); *C. punctatum* (I,H)

**Dendrobium aggregatum* (C,I); **D.* x *Ainsworthii* (C,I); **D. anosmum* (I,H); *D. bigibbum* and its var. **Phalaenopsis* (I,H) and hybrids (I,H); *D. fimbriatum* and var. *oculatum* (I,H); *D. moschatum* (I,H); **D. nobile* and its many hybrids (C,I); **D. Pierardii* (I,H)

**Dendrochilum glumaceum* (I,H); **D. filiforme* (I,H)

**Diacrium bicornutum* (I,H); **D. bilamellatum* (I,H)

Epicattleya x *Nebo* (I,H); *EC.* x *Orpeti* (I,H)

**Epidendrum atropurpureum* (I,H); **E. ciliare* (I,H); **E. cochleatum* (I,H); **E. fragrans* (I,H); *E. ibaguense* (I,H); *E. nemorale* (C,I); **E.* x *O'Brienianum* (I,H); **E. radiatum* (I,H); **E. Stamfordianum* (I,H); **E. tampense* (I,H)

Eria hyacinthoides (I,H); **E. javanica* (I,H)

Gomesa planifolia (I,H)

Laelia albida (C,I); *L. anceps* (C,I); *L. crispa* (I,H); *L. pumila* (I,H); *L. purpurata* (I,H); *L. rubescens* (C,I); *L. speciosa* (C,I)

Laeliocattleya x Aphrodite (I); *LC. x Britannia* (I,H); *LC. x Callistoglossa* (I); *LC. x Canhamiana* and var. *alba* (I); *LC. x Marie Webb* (I); *LC. x Princess Margaret* (I)

Leptotes bicolor (I,H)

Lockhartia acuta (I,H); *L. Oerstedii* (I,H)

Lycaste aromatica (C,I); *L. brevispatha* (I,H); *L. cruenta* (C,I); *L. virginalis* (C,I)

Masdevallia Chimaera (C); *M. erythrochaete* (C,I); *M. tovarensis* (C,I)

Maxillaria crassifolia (I,H); *M. luteo-alba* (I,H); *M. tenuifolia* (C,I,H); *M. variabilis* (I,H)

Miltonia flavescens (I,H); *M. Roezlii* (I,H); *M. spectabilis* and var. *Moreliana* (I,H)

Mormodes igneum (I,H)

Neobenthamia gracilis (I,H)

Odontoglossum crispum (C); *O. grande* (C,I); *O. pendulum* (C,I); *O. Schlieperianum* (I,H)

Oncidium flexuosum (I,H); *O. Lanceanum* (I,H); *O. longifolium* (I,H); *O. varicosum* var. *Rogersii* (I,H); *O. Wentworthianum* (I,H)

Paphiopedilum callosum (I,H); *P. insigne* and var. *Sanderae* (C,I); *P. x Harrisianum* (I,H); *P. x Leeanum* (C,I,H); *P. x Maudiae* (I,H)

Peristeria elata (I,H)

Phaius Tankervilliae (C,I,H)

Pholidota imbricata (I,H)

Phragmipedium caudatum (I,H); *P. x grande* (I,H); *P. x Sedenii* (I,H)

Pleurothallis gelida (I); *P. Grobyi* (I,H); *P. rubens* (I,H); *P. ophiocephala* (I,H)

Polystachya luteola (I,H)

Rhyncholaelia Digbyana (I,H); *R. glauca* (I,H)

Rodriguezia secunda (I,H); *R. venusta* (I,H)

Schomburgkia (Laelia) tibicinis (H); *S. undulata* (I,H)

Sophronitis cernua (C,I); *S. coccinea* (C,I)

Spathoglottis plicata (I,H); *S. hybrids* (I,H)

Stanhopea graveolens (I,H); *S. Wardii* (I,H)

Stenoglottis longifolia (C,I)

Trichopilia suavis (C,I); **T. tortilis* (I,H)
*Zygopetalum intermedium (C,I)

Section II. Monopodial Types

*Aerides odoratum (I,H)

*Angraecum distichum (I,H); *A. eburneum* (I,H); **A. Eichlerianum* (I,H); *A. sesquipedale* (I,H)

*Phalaenopsis amabilis (I,H); *P. Lueddemanniana* (I,H); **P. Schilleriana* (I,H); **P. hybrids* (I,H)

Renanthera coccinea (I,H); *R. Imschootiana* (I,H); *R. monachica* (I,H)

Vanda coerulea (C,I); **V. lamellata* and var. **Boxallii* (I,H); *V. x Miss Joaquim* (H); **V. tricolor* and var. **suavis* (I,H); **various Vanda hybrids* (I,H)

Vandopsis lissochiloides (H)

SPECIALIZATION

Perhaps the most important fact for the beginner to bear in mind, when starting his collection of orchids, is to keep his plants in a single basic temperature group for ease of control. This means that the novice should not attempt, initially at least, to grow cool, intermediate, and hot types in his presumably limited space. Although many orchids are amenable to conditions that are technically unsuited to them, the amateur will have far fewer difficulties if he concentrates in the beginning on plants belonging to a single category of growth requirements (see page 93).

For example, the hobbyist may be particularly (and logically) attracted to the numerous members of the *Cattleya* group, almost all of which fall into the intermediate temperature grouping. With these, he may grow several thousand species and hybrids outside of this particular alliance as well, certainly enough to furnish him with good subjects for an indefinite period. Intermediate orchids are the best for cultivation in the home, in an "indoor greenhouse" or comparable interior apparatus, or in a small greenhouse in temperate climates, since their cultural requirements are less rigid than those of cool or hot types. The lists on pages 93 to 96 tell exactly which of the commonly grown orchids fall into this category, and are therefore especially suitable for starting a collection.

As soon as the cultivation of these relatively simple intermediate types has been mastered, the enthusiast will doubtless wish to go on to the slightly more complicated cool and hot forms (see the above mentioned lists also for these plants). When this move is decided upon, it will probably be necessary (or at least advisable) to make an addition to the growing-quarters, either by partitioning off a portion of the greenhouse, or by installing another "indoor greenhouse" capable of maintaining, respectively, lower or higher temperatures than those previously required.

ABBREVIATIONS AND SYMBOLS USED

In the succeeding pages of this work, abbreviations and symbols are used for words and conditions that are many times repeated in the descriptions. Here is a list of these abbreviations:

caps. = capsule, or "seed-pod"
col. = column, or gynostemium
diam. = diameter
dors. = dorsal
fl. = flower
fld. = flowered
fls. = flowers
infl. = inflorescence
infls. = inflorescences
lat. = lateral
lats. = lateral (sepals)
lb. = lobe

lbd. = lobed
lbs. = lobes
lf. = leaf
lvs. = leaves
midlb. = midlobe
pb. = pseudobulb
pbs. = pseudobulbs
pls. = plants
ps. = petals
rac. = raceme
racs. = racemes
rhiz. = rhizome

segm. = segment	ss. = sepals
segms. = segments	st. = stem
sep. = sepal	sts. = stems
sp. = species (singular)	subvar. = subvariety
spp. = species (plural)	var. = variety

The following symbols have also been used in this work: *x* designates that the plant under discussion is of hybrid origin; × indicates the two (or more) parents of a hybrid

The letters (C), (I), and (H) designate theoretically ideal temperature requirements for a genus or one of its component species or variants. The symbol (C) indicates that cool conditions should prevail (that is, average night temperatures of 45–50° F. during the cool months); (I) indicates intermediate (55–65° F.); and (H) warm or tropical conditions (65–70° F.) or more). Combinations of one or more symbols enclosed parenthetically — as (C,I), (I,H), (C,I,H), etc.— indicate that the temperature requirements of the genus, species, or hybrid under consideration are variable. Individual conditions, especially in the tropics, will determine which range of temperature will best suit the plant.

THE PRINCIPAL CULTIVATED ORCHIDS

ACAMPE
(ah-*kam*-pee)

About 13 species of *Acampe* are known. These are epiphytic or rather rarely lithophytic orchids of the general *Vanda* group. They are widely distributed in the tropical regions of Africa and Asia, but are uncommon in our collections at this time, though they are interesting, albeit mostly small-flowered plants. The leaves are usually very fleshy or leathery and somewhat recurved. The generally small or medium-sized, fragrant, waxen flowers are borne in dense cylindrical racemes or tight heads.

CULTURE: As for the tropical Vandas. (I, H)

A. longifolia (lon-ji-*foe*-lee-ah)   (Himalayas to Malay Peninsula)

Sts. robust, often branched, frequently rather gracefully curving, to more than 2' tall, usually densely leafy. Lvs. thick, stiffly ascending, to about 8" long, tongue-shaped. Infls. erect, sometimes shortly branched, to 4" tall, the fls. very crowded, mostly opening successively over a relatively long period of time. Fls. fleshy, not opening fully, about ¾" across at most, rather delicately fragrant, the ss. and ps. pale lemon-yellow with narrow crimson cross-bars and spots. Lip complex, white with a few purple spots, saclike basally. Summer. (I,H)

Acampe multiflora

GEORGE FULLER

ACINETA
(ah-si-*neh*-tah)

Acineta contains about 12 species of robust epiphytic (very rarely lithophytic) orchids in the American tropics, ranging from southern Mexico to Ecuador and Venezuela. The genus is allied to *Peristeria*, and the rarely cultivated species have strongly pendulous, often elongate racemes of large and spectacular flowers borne from the bases of prominent fleshy pseudobulbs. Although splendid plants, these are regrettably rare orchids in our collections at this time.

CULTURE: As for *Stanhopea*. (I,H)

A. chrysantha (kry-*san*-thah)   (Costa Rica; Panama)

Pbs. clustered, egg-shaped, somewhat compressed, strongly furrowed, often yellowish, to 5" long. Lvs. 3 or 4, to almost 2' long, very heavy-textured. Infls. elongate, pendulous, to 3′ long, rather densely few-to many-fld., the fls. mostly all opening at once. Fls. fleshy, waxy, highly fragrant, cuplike, to more than 2″ across, rather long-lived, the ss. usually bright yellow, the ps. yellow spotted with red or crimson

Acineta chrysantha

The Orchid Journal

toward base and margins, the very complex lip golden-yellow, more or less spotted and marked with red and reddish brown. Spring. (I,H)

AERIDES
(ah-*er*-i-deez)

This justifiably popular genus consists of some 60 species of often very handsome, many-flowered epiphytic or lithophytic orchids. These occur over a vast region, extending from China and Japan to New Guinea, with the majority of the known species occurring in the Himalayas, Burma, and Indonesia. Basically resembling Vandas in habit, they produce generally elongate, very dense, columnar racemes of waxen, highly fragrant flowers, whose appearance gives rise to the vernacular name of "Foxtail Orchids."

CULTURE: As for *Vanda*. (I,H)

A. odoratum (oh-do-*rah*-tum)   (China to New Guinea)

Highly variable in all parts. Old specimens to 5′ tall, often profusely branched. Lvs. numerous, to 10″ long and 2″ broad, leathery, glossy. Usually several infls. at once, arching to pendulous, to 2′ long, cylindrical, more or less densely many-fld. Fls. 1–2″ long, very fragrant, waxy, the ss. and ps. white with an amethyst-purple or magenta apical blotch, the funnel-shaped lip prolonged at base into a hornlike spur, 3-lbd., the lat. lbs. erect, white, sometimes with a faint light purple flush and some scattered purple spots; midlb. small, white with a broad purple median band. Mostly fall, especially Sept.–Oct. (I,H)

A. quinquevulnerum (kwin-kwe-*vul*-neh-rum)   (Philippines)

Similar to *A. odoratum*, often somewhat more robust. Infls. to more than 18″ long, usually gracefully down-arching, densely many-fld. Fls. 1″ long or less, very fragrant, lasting about two weeks, the dors.

Aerides quinquevulnerum

sep. and ps. similar, white with a vivid amethyst-purple apical blotch and some purple spots scattered over the remaining area; lat. ss. oblique, similar in color. Lip 3-lbd., prolonged at base into an incurved, hornlike, green spur; lat. lbs. erect, white faintly dotted with purple; midlb. dark amethyst-purple, the margins toothed. Mostly Aug.–Nov. (I,H)

AERANGIS
(ah-er-*an*-giss)

Aerangis contains upwards of 70 species, these mostly epiphytic (rarely lithophytic) orchids inhabiting Tropical Africa, Madagascar, and adjacent island groups. Related to *Angraecum*, they are for the most part very handsome, sometimes elegantly spectacular plants which are as yet seldom seen in any save the most comprehensive collections. Like so many orchids of this alliance, Aerangis should be far more widely grown and better appreciated by hobbyists.

CULTURE: As for *Vanda*. (I,H)

A. Ellisii (*el*-iss-ee-eye)   (Madagascar)

St. to 10″ tall, more than ½″ in diam. Lvs. very heavily leathery, narrowly oblong, 5–8″ long, usually about 2″ broad. Infls. arching at

Aerangis Kotschyana

VEITCH

first, eventually becoming pendulous, to 2′ long, bearing about 15–25 fls. above the greenish pedicellate ovaries. Fls. waxy, fragrant of gardenias, long-lived, to 2½″ across, snow-white, the slender, awl-shaped, twisted spur 6–8″ long, flushed apically with brownish or pale orange-red. Summer, mostly July–Sept. (H)

ANGRAECUM
(an-*grye*-kum)

The genus *Angraecum* consists of more than 200 species, only a very few of which have as yet made their way into our collections, even though the group includes some of the finest of all orchidaceous plants. Largely epiphytic (rarely lithophytic) in habit, they are primarily restricted in their distribution to Africa and nearby islands, but outlying representatives of the genus occur as far afield as the Philippines and Ceylon. Extremely diverse in vegetative structure, the often abundant flowers are starlike and generally white in color.

CULTURE: As for *Vanda*, with tropical conditions being essential for the majority of the cultivated species. (I,H)

A. distichum (*diss*-tik-um) (Tropical West Africa)

Sts. clustered, often forming dense entangled masses, to 6″ long. Lvs. very numerous, fleshy, glossy bright green, overlapping, vaguely triangular, usually only about ¼″ long. Infls. very short, 1-fld., often numerous at one time. Fls. inverted, highly fragrant of narcissus, glit-

Angraecum distichum

GEORGE FULLER

tering pure white, about ¼″ across, lasting for about two weeks. Usually fall–winter, but often virtually everblooming when well grown. (I,H)

A. eburneum (ee-*bur*-nee-um) (Mascarene Islands)

Very robust, to 6′ tall. Lvs. thickly set, rigidly leathery, to 3′ long and 3″ broad, gracefully arching or horizontally arranged. Infls. often several at once, ascending or horizontal, stout, to 4′ long, densely many-fld., the fls. neatly arranged in two ranks, inverted. Fls. very fragrant, heavily waxy, long-lived, to 3″ long, the ss. and ps. greenish-white, the large lip pure white, the elongate awl-shaped spur with a greenish tip, to 4″ long. Mostly fall–early winter. (H)

A. sesquipedale (sess-kwi-peh-*dah*-lee) (Madagascar)

St. usually solitary, usually less than 2′ tall, woody below, very leafy above. Lvs. closely arranged, dark green, often somewhat white-powdery, leathery, wavy-margined, to about 1′ long and to 2″ broad. Infls. usually horizontal to down-arching, stout, 2–4-fld., to about 1′ long, the keeled bracts brownish. Fls. very fleshy, heavily waxy, fragrant, long-lived, to 7″ in diam., ivory-white, star-shaped, but the lip broader than the other segments, and with a greenish spur to almost 1′ long. Mostly winter. (I,H)

ANGULOA
(an-gyoo-*low*-ah)

About 10 species make up the genus *Anguloa*, known by the few fortunate collectors who possess them as the "Tulip Orchids," because of the similarity of the blossoms to those popular garden bulbs. Terrestrial or epiphytic in habit, the Anguloas inhabit the Andean regions of Colombia, Venezuela, Ecuador, and Peru. They are closely allied to *Lycaste*. The typically large, heavy-textured, solitary flowers are cup-shaped, very intricate in structure, headily fragrant, and variable in coloration.

CULTURE: Mostly high-elevation plants, the Anguloas do best in the cool *Odontoglossum-Miltonia* greenhouse. In perfectly drained pots they will thrive. A suggested compost for them is made up of about 3 parts of good rich loam or sifted soil, 1½ parts slightly chopped osmunda fiber, about ½ part fresh sphagnum moss, and a rather small quantity of dried, shredded oak leaves. A bright and airy spot is necessary, for the adult plants delight in considerable quantities of diffused light. When the new growths are being produced, large amounts of water should be given, but upon maturation of the pseudobulbs a strict rest-period of several weeks' duration is absolutely essential for proper production of flowers. Heavy feeders, Anguloas may to good advantage be fertilized at frequent intervals. (C,I)

A. Clowesii (klo-*wess*-ee-eye) (Colombia; Venezuela)

Pbs. cylindric-oblong, 5–6″ tall, becoming furrowed with age. Lvs. deciduous in time, to 2′ long, prominently folded. Infls. often multiple,

1-fld., to almost 1' tall. Fls. with an odd medicinal odor, subglobose, very waxy, to 3″ long, rather compressed on the sides, bright citron- or golden-yellow, the very complex lip freely movable, varying in color from cream-white to orange-yellow. Several attractive color variants are known. Spring–early summer. (C,I)

The Orchid Journal

Anguloa Clowesii

Anguloa uniflora

A. uniflora (yoo-ni-*floe*-rah)   (Colombia to Peru)

Pbs. angular, rather elongate, 4–7″ tall. Lvs. heavy, to more than 2′ long, strongly folded. Infls. often very numerous from a single growth, 1-fld., 6–10″ tall. Fls. rather open for the genus, objectionably candy-scented, very waxy and long-lived, to 4″ long and wide, cup-shaped, in the typical phase waxen white or cream-white, usually flushed and dotted inside with pale or bright pink or rose-pink. Mostly early spring. (C,I)

ANOECTOCHILUS
(ah-nek-*taw*-ki-luss)

The genus *Anoectochilus* contains about 20 species of incredibly beauti-ful plants, known as the "Jewel Orchids." They are rare in our col-lections and notoriously difficult to grow. Primarily terrestrials (a few of them sometimes occur on very mossy rocks or on the bases of moss-hung trees), they are indigenous over a broad region, extending from the Himalayas to New Guinea, with many species being found in Indonesia. Unlike the vast majority of orchids, these are not cultivated primarily for their flowers—which are usually small and rather insignificant—but rather for the magnificent, variegated, velvety foliage.

CULTURE: The cultural requirements of this genus (and its allies) are difficult to formulate briefly, since almost every single component species seems to require slightly different treatment from its fellows. The principal requisites, however, are the following: (1) a perfectly drained compost, as rich and porous as possible; (2) high temperatures and saturated humidity at all times; (3) shade from direct sun-exposure; and (4) no disturbance of the root-system. A compost made up of equal parts of shredded osmunda or tree-fern fiber, chopped sphagnum moss, porous, pea-size gravel or crushed pumice, and leaf-mould, has been found to be satisfactory. Greenhouse culture is obligatory, and many authorities suggest growing these very fragile and temperamental orchids under bell-jars to assure adequately high humidity and to protect them from abrupt temperature changes. (H)

A. Roxburghii (rox-*burg*-ee-eye)   (Himalayas)

Lvs. few, forming a rather loose rosette, to 2″ long and 1½″ broad,

Anoectochilus Roxburghii

GEORGE FULLER

soft-textured, very dark velvety-green with a very complex branching network of golden veins, the median part of each lf. occupied by a distinct golden zone, the margins flushed with reddish. Infls. erect, about 1' tall, few-fld. toward apex. Fls. less than ¾" long, complex, the ss. and ps. greenish, the lip usually white. Summer. (H)

ANSELLIA
(an-*sel*-ee-ah)

Only a single species of *Ansellia* is known, this an excessively variable and very spectacular epiphytic or lithophytic orchid native to Tropical Africa. It is as yet very infrequently encountered in our collections, but its myriad flowers—borne on usually tall, attractively branched sprays—are handsome and last in perfection for more than a month. The blotched, sleek appearance of the blossoms has given this genus the common name of "Leopard Orchid."

CULTURE: Ansellias are easily grown, even by the novice hobbyist, provided sufficient heat and humidity can be afforded them in the greenhouse. Best given a very bright situation in rather large, perfectly drained pots, they do especially well when tightly potted in straight osmunda fiber. While in active growth they benefit by liberal applications of water, but need a rest-period of about a month upon completion of the new pseudobulbs for optimum flower production. Heavy feeders, they should be fertilized liberally and regularly. (H)

A. africana (af-ri-*kah*-nah) (Tropical and South Africa)

Common synonyms are *A. confusa*, *A. congoensis* and *A. gigantea*. Pbs. stemlike, almost cylindrical in most specimens, sometimes club-

Ansellia africana

The Orchid Journal

shaped or spindle-shaped, to more than 2′ tall, often yellowish. Lvs. borne mostly near apex of pb., thinly leathery, to about 1′ long. Infls. terminal, often very stout, to 3′ long, rather loosely many-fld., generally branched. Fls. about 2½″ long in the largest phases, spreading, rather delicately fragrant during the hot hours of the day, lasting a month or more, the ss. and ps. varying in color from almost green to bright yellow, more or less spotted, blotched or transversely barred with pale or dark chocolate-brown. Lip 3-lbd., the lat. lbs. erect, all parts yellow or yellowish with dark or pale brown veins, the disc with several yellow keels. Winter–summer. (H)

ARACHNIS
(ah-*rak*-niss)

The genus *Arachnis* contains about 17 species, these widespread in the area extending from the Himalayas to New Guinea and the Solomon Islands. The group is allied to *Vanda*, *Renanthera*, and the like, and several of its handsomer members are in more or less frequent cultivation, particularly by orchidists in the tropics. Some of the Arachnis are very tall, vinelike plants, while others are short-stemmed, much like a *Vanda*. The multicolored flowers are generally produced in considerable numbers, and their strange form has given them the common name of "Scorpion Orchids."

CULTURE: The tall-growing, vinelike species of *Arachnis* do best if grown in specially prepared, raised beds, in a perfectly drained compost of the richest possible components, this to include shredded osmunda or tree-fern fiber, sphagnum moss, gritty white sand, and manure or other fertilizing materials; addition of fibrous loam, leaf-mould, and perhaps even portions of bark preparation should also be made in moderation. Full exposure to the sun is required in most instances for proper production of flowers, and water should be afforded in large amounts at all times. If grown in pots, under glass, the plants must be subjected to as much bright sun as possible, and even then they usually will not flower until they have reached a considerable size; large containers, with copious and perfect drainage, should be used to accommodate the rampant root-systems. Regular and liberal applications of fertilizers prove beneficial to these robust, heavy-feeding orchids. The short-stemmed kinds of Arachnis thrive when grown like the tropical Vandas. (I,H)

A. flos-aeris (*floes-air*-iss)   (Malay Peninsula to Borneo)

Often known by the synonym *A. moschifera*. Sts. stout, climbing, to more than 15′ tall, often branched, the lvs. rather distant. Lvs. to 7″ long and 2″ broad, narrowed gradually toward the 2-lbd. apex, rather leathery. Infls. simple or branching, ascending or drooping, to about 4′ long, the fls. rather numerous but widely spaced. Fls. to more than 4″ long and 3½″ wide, fleshy, glossy, with a strong musky odor, long-lived. Ss. and ps. pale yellow-green with broad and irregular dark

REG S. DAVIS   C. K. KUEH

Arachnis flos-aeris   *Arachnis x Maggie Oei*

purple-brown bars and spots. Lip pale yellow-green, purple-brown, and dull purple, complex in structure. Mostly during the fall months, but often almost everblooming in the tropics. (H)

A. Maingayi (main-*gay*-eye)   (Malay Peninsula; Borneo)

Rather similar in all parts to *A. flos-aeris*. Sts. turning red-brown with age. Lvs. stiff, nearly straight, the edges recurved and slightly toothed near base, about 5″ long. Infls. and fl.-shape much as in the allied species, the fls. slightly smaller. Ss. and ps. whitish or faintly pink-ish with bands and blotches of pink or light purple. Lip whitish or pinkish. Mostly summer. (H)

ARUNDINA
(ah-run-*dee*-nah)

Although several have been described, only one species of *Arundina* appears to be valid, according to contemporary orchidologists. This is a handsome and variable tall-growing terrestrial orchid ranging from southern China and the Himalayas throughout Malaysia, Indonesia, and adjacent areas to the islands of the Pacific. Arundinas somewhat resemble thin-leaved Sobralias in appearance, and bear handsome but short-lasting flowers much like small Cattleyas. They are relatively uncommon in collections outside of the tropics, but are very attractive and should be far better known.

CULTURE: These plants are best grown in specially prepared beds, such as are suggested for the tall-growing, viny species of *Arachnis* (which see). If kept in pots, flowering is often seriously curtailed. Tropical conditions are required at all times, with abundant water and high humidity. (H)

A. graminifolia (gra-mi-ni-*foe*-lee-ah)   (Range of the genus)

Also known as *A. bambusifolia* and *A. densa*, both synonyms. Sts. close together on the rhiz., slender, to 8′ tall, leafy throughout. Lvs. rather grass-like, to 1′ long, glossy. Infls. terminal, with large bracts,

Arundina graminifolia

gradually elongating and producing a succession of fls. 1 or 2 at a time, each lasting about 3 days. Fls. delicately fragrant, to 2½″ long, the lat. ss. closer together behind the lip than in a *Cattleya*. Ss. and ps. white to pale rose-mauve, of a glittering texture. Lip tubular at base, usually vivid rose-purple at apex, the throat paler, veined with purple, with a yellow patch on the disc. The pure white, yellow-throated forma *alba* is sometimes encountered, but is very rare. Flowers are produced throughout the year, and the plant is often almost everblooming when well grown. (H)

ASCOCENTRUM
(ass-koe-*sen*-trum)

Somewhat allied to *Vanda* and its relatives, *Ascocentrum* contains 9 species of smallish but very spectacular orchids which are as yet infrequently encountered in our collections. Epiphytes or rarely lithophytes in nature, they inhabit the area ranging from southern China (Yunnan), Formosa, and the Philippines to Java and Borneo. When seen in cultivation, these charming plants are almost invariably found under the confusing generic name of *Saccolabium*, which is applicable to a totally distinct group of orchids.

CULTURE: As for the tropical Vandas. Pot-culture is recommended for best results. (I,H)

A. miniatum (min-ee-*ah*-tum)   (Himalayas to Indonesia)

St. usually less than 4″ tall, thick, woody, obscured by persistent lf.-sheaths. Lvs. narrow, very rigidly fleshy, 3–8″ long, usually less than

Ascocentrum miniatum

REG S. DAVIS

½″ broad, strongly keeled beneath. Infls. erect, to 5″ tall, very densely many-fld., cylindrical. Fls. about ¾″ across, variable in hue from bright orange through orange-yellow to vivid vermilion-red, the lip with a slender cylindric spur. Col. very short, with a purple anther-cap. Spring–early summer. (I,H)

ASPASIA
(ass-*pay*-zee-ah)

This genus contains about 10 species of showy, medium-sized epiphytic orchids which are nowadays rather popular with collectors. The genus, which is native to Central and South America, is allied to *Oncidium* and *Brassia*. Recently it has been used in the production of some lovely hybrids.

CULTURE: Aspasias should be grown in pots of tightly packed, well-drained osmunda, in a rather warm and moist situation, with water given sparingly after the completion of the new growths. If given too much sun, the foliage tends to become unsightly through burning. (I,H)

A. epidendroides (ep-i-den-*droy*-deez)   (Guatemala to Colombia)

Pbs. ellipsoidal, compressed, stalked, to 6″ tall. Lvs. leathery, paired, to 1′ long and 2″ broad. Fls. few, in erect racemes to 10″ tall, 1½″

Aspasia epidendroides

DRAWING BY G. W. DILLON

long the ss. greenish with broad transverse bands of brown or brownish lavender, the ps. pale lavender to greenish-brown, the large lip white with purple or lavender central markings. Summer. (I,H)

A. principissa (prin-si-*pi*-sah)   (Costa Rica; Panama)

Similar to the other described species, but with larger fls. (about 3″ long) on a less robust plant. Fls. faintly fragrant, lasting well, the ss. and broader ps. pale green or yellow-green with longitudinal brown or tan stripes. Lip large, wavy marginally, wide-spreading, cream-white aging to pale yellow, more or less streaked on the middle with darker yellow. Late spring–summer. (I,H)

BIFRENARIA
(bif-ren-*ah*-ree-ah)

Bifrenaria consists of about 11 species of variable and often highly spectacular orchids, all endemic to Brazil, insofar as is known. In the wild they inhabit trees and mossy rock-outcroppings, where their customarily angular, glossy pseudobulbs and lacquered leaves often form huge clusters. The flowers in this genus are generally large and of singularly striking structure, yet Bifrenarias are today extremely scarce in our collections.

CULTURE: As for *Lycaste*. Most of the species thrive when fully exposed to sun. (I,H)

B. Harrisoniae (har-i-*son*-ee-eye)   (Brazil)

Pbs. clustered, broadly egg-shaped, vaguely or strongly 4-angled, 2–3″ tall, often flushed (especially near apex) with red-brown. Lf.

Bifrenaria Harrisoniae

VEITCH

solitary, leathery, rather rigid, shiny to 1′ long and 5″ broad. Infls. usually paired from latest-formed pb.-bases, 1–2-fld., usually about 2″ tall. Fls. about 3″ in diam., very waxy, heavily fragrant, long-lasting, very handsome, the spurlike chin prominent; fl.-color variable, but usually with the ss. and ps. ivory-white (sometimes yellowish or green-ish yellow, apically flushed with reddish), the large ornate lip 3-lbd., rich wine-purple to magenta-red, usually veined darker, hairy in part, the disc very hairy, yellow or orange-yellow. Col. large, club-shaped, white. Spring–early summer. (I,H)

BLETIA
(*blet*-ee-ah)

This is a genus of about 50 species, all natives of the Americas, rang-ing from south-central Florida and Mexico (the center of develop-ment) to Brazil and Peru. As yet but little known by orchidists, *Bletia* contains a remarkable number of handsome and often spectacular, usually terrestrial orchids of singularly facile cultural requirements. Though the individual blossoms—borne on tall wandlike stems from the bases of the frequently partially buried, cormlike pseudobulbs—are seldom long-lived, they are produced in abundance over a long period of time.

CULTURE: If grown in pots, treatment such as that suggested for *Phaius* is to be utilized. In sufficiently equable climates, Bletias do very well in outdoor beds, in the manner of the viny types of *Arachnis*. (I,H)

B. catenulata (kah-ten-yoo-*lah*-tah) (Peru; Brazil)

Corms to 4″ in diam., flattened from above, furrowed and consid-erably wrinkled with age. Lvs. long-stalked, few, to 2′ long, about 4″ broad, folded. Infls. to 3′ tall, rather loosely 3–8-fld. Fls. about 2″ across, showy, opening wider than most of the other spp., the ss. and ps. rose-magenta, the large lip dark rose-magenta, the margins crisped and wavy, often paler, the crests usually whitish or cream-white. Spring–summer. (I,H)

B. purpurea (poor-poor-*ee*-ah) (Florida to N. South America)

Common synonyms are *B. tuberosa* and *B. verecunda*. Corms com-pressed from above, about 1½″ in maximum diam., often produced in rather long chains, either subterranean or partially exposed. Lvs. few, stalked basally, narrow to rather broad, folded, to 3′ long, usually less than 2″ broad. Infls. to 5′ tall, a simple or branched rac. at the apex, few-to many-fld., the fls. usually opening successively over a period of more than a month. Fls. about 1¾″ across in the largest phases, varying in color from pink to rose-purple (very rarely with the ss. and ps. white), not opening fully, the ps. usually lying parallel alongside the col., forming an open hood over the lip, this usually darker in color than other segms., with 5–7 yellowish keels on the disc. Mostly spring–early summer. (I,H)

BLETILLA
(blet-*il*-ah)

Bletilla is a genus of 7 known species, these largely terrestrial (rarely rock-dwelling) orchids native to China, Japan, and Formosa, only one of which is in cultivation at this time, and this one usually under the erroneous name of *Bletia hyacinthina*. This *Bletilla* is commonly offered by dealers in garden bulbs, and with its attractive sprays of showy, intricate blossoms, borne above handsome folded foliage, it forms a welcome addition to every collection.

CULTURE: This is one of the easiest of all orchids to grow, and is almost completely hardy, even in temperate regions. The plants are most successful when kept confined to big pots (8″ or 9″ size), perfectly drained, in a compost consisting of rich garden soil, loam, rotted leaves, and gritty white sand, with some manure added with a liberal hand. Often the plants will not blossom until they become potbound, hence they should be disturbed only when absolutely essential. They need to be kept moist while actively growing, but when the foliage commences to wither, water should be withheld for the most part until the new shoots begin to appear in the spring. *Bletilla* also does well in outdoor beds, to be treated much in the manner of garden bulbs, such as tulips, narcissi, except that they should not be dug up for the winter. (C,I)

B. striata (stry-*ah*-tah)   (China; Japan)

Pbs. roundish, compressed, typically subterranean. Lvs. to 1′ tall, rarely more, tightly stalked at base, folded above, light or dark green, rarely variegated with white or cream-white. Infls. solitary, appearing from the middle of the expanding shoots, to 3′ tall in particularly robust specimens. Fls. to 12 (generally fewer), opening successively, 1–2″ across, rather nodding on the stalk, the ss. and ps. typically rose-purple or magenta-purple. Lip darker, with very dark purple, raised, median keels, the throat cream-white or glossy yellow. Mostly June–July. (C,I)

BRASSAVOLA
(brah-*sah*-voe-lah)

The Brassavolas, numbering about 15 species, are justly popular orchids, with flowers that are usually abundant and showy. The genus, which contains mostly epiphytes or lithophytes, extends from Jamaica and Mexico to Bolivia, Brazil, and Peru. Most of the species have cylindrical, stemlike pseudobulbs topped by a solitary, also cylindrical, fleshy leaf. *Brassavola* is closely allied to *Laelia* and to the segregate genus *Rhyncholaelia* (to which the old *B. glauca* and *B. Digbyana* have been added). These easy-to-grow orchids should form an integral part of every collection.

CULTURE: In general as for *Cattleya*. The commonly grown Brassavolas do best and are more floriferous when grown in full sun. (I,H)

B. cucullata (kyoo-kyoo-*lah*-tah)

(West Indies; Mexico to N. South America)

Sts. to 5″ tall, slender. Lf. solitary normally, terete, whiplike, fleshy, to almost 2′ long, mostly pendulous or at least down-arching. Fl. solitary (rarely paired), fragrant, long-lasting, to 7″ long in robust forms

H. TEUSCHER   FLORENCE B. JOHNSON

Brassavola cucullata   *Brassavola nodosa*

in which the ss. and ps. are held out, these segments usually drooping, varying from white to yellowish with white margins to greenish white, sometimes red-flushed at apex, narrow, long-pointed. Lip white or whitish, heart-shaped, fringed basally. Pedicellate ovary with its stalk to as much as 8″ long. Throughout the year, but mostly in winter. (I,H)

B. nodosa (noe-*doe*-sah)   (Tropical America)

Pls. erect to pendulous, extremely variable in vegetative and floral dimensions, and, to a lesser degree, in shape, the pls. in large forms to 15" tall. Sts. cylindrical, to 6" tall. Lf. solitary, mostly erect, very fleshy, grooved on upper surface, to more than 1' long and 1" broad (usually much narrower and sometimes almost cylindrical). Infls. to 8" long, 1–6-fld. Fls. to 3½" across, extremely and deliciously fragrant at night, long-lived, the ss. and ps. narrow, varying from pale green or yellowish to almost pure white, the large, basally tubular lip white, often with some vague purplish spots on the inside of the curving tube. Throughout the year, often almost everblooming. (I,H)

BRASSIA
(*brass*-ee-ah)

The Brassias are the best known of the "Spider Orchids," characterized by elongate flowers (sometimes one foot in length) of startling color combinations and exotic fragrances. About 30 species are known, these mostly epiphytic plants ranging from South Florida and Mexico to Peru and Brazil. They are popular with present-day orchidists, being readily brought into a handsome flowering state even by the novice collector. The genus is somewhat allied to *Oncidium*, and some remarkable hybrids (called Brassidiums) have been made between the two groups.

CULTURE: As for *Aspasia*. (I,H)

B. Gireoudiana (jee-ree-ood-ee-*ah*-nah)   (Costa Rica; Panama)

Pbs. flattened, to 6" tall and 1½" broad, usually glossy. Lvs. 2 or 3, glossy dark green, somewhat leathery, to more than 1' long. Infls. often paired, to 1½" long, 3–12-fld. Fls. long-lasting, very fragrant, 8–12" long, the ss. and ps. rather stiffly spreading, yellow or greenish yellow, with a few irregular bars and blotches of dark brown near the base. Lip usually brighter yellow, also marked with brown, the basal calli white or cream-white flushed with bright yellow and dark brown. Spring. (I)

B. verrucosa (ve-roo-*koe*-sah)   (Mexico to N. South America)

A familiar synonym is *B. brachiata*. Somewhat similar to *B. Gireoudiana* in habit, but the very dark green pbs. not especially flattened. Infls. arching, to 2½' long, bearing up to 24 blossoms. Fls. 4–6" long, spreading, fragrant, lasting well, with narrow segments. Ss. and ps. usually greenish, spotted (mostly near the base) with black-purple. Lip large, white or white with a greenish suffusion, with few to numerous black-green warts mostly near base. Summer. (I,H)

The Orchid Journal

Brassia Gireoudiana

BROUGHTONIA
(braw-*toe*-nee-ah)

This is a monotypic genus of dwarf, spectacular epiphytic orchids from the island of Jamaica, often confused with the closely allied *Cattleyopsis,* and as yet somewhat rare in cultivation, though they should be far better known by orchidists. The clustered pseudobulbs are rounded and compressed, and bear short, rigid, very thick leaves. The showy blossoms are produced on slender, arching, elongated racemes or panicles, last for a long time, and are among the most vividly hued of all orchids.

CULTURE: Broughtonias should be grown under conditions similar to those afforded the warm-growing pseudobulbous Epidendrums, preferably on osmunda or tree-fern slabs, or in baskets tightly packed with osmunda. They are generally most successful and flower most profusely when grown into large specimens. They delight in warmth and in quantities of sunshine. The roots should never be kept wet, for rapid rotting may occur. In warm countries Broughtonias may to good advantage be grown on trees or rocks in the outdoor garden, fully exposed to the sun. (H)

B. sanguinea (sang-*win*-ee-ah) (Jamaica)

Habit as in the genus, dwarf, cluster-forming. Pbs. usually less than 2" tall. Lvs. to 4" long, very rigid, often grayish green in color. Infls.

Broughtonia sanguinea

ROD MCLELLAN COMPANY

to 3' long, gracefully arching or erect, bearing 12 or more fls. Fls. to 1" across, rounded, resembling a diminutive *Cattleya* in shape, rather long-lived. Ss. and ps. very rich crimson-magenta. Lip similar in color, with darker veins over all of its surface. Winter–early spring. (H)

BULBOPHYLLUM
(bul-bow-*fil*-um)

This is the largest of all orchid genera, with an estimated 2000 species dispersed in virtually all of the tropical and subtropical parts of the globe, the distributional center being in New Guinea. They are typically epiphytic plants of great complexity, seldom seen in cultivation, because of the characteristically small (often minute) flowers. Usually the Bulbophyllums have conical or globose pseudobulbs borne on a more or less creeping rhizome, with a solitary apical leaf; the inflorescences are basal for the most part, and bear few to many intricate, often quite handsome blossoms. In this genus the sepals are mostly much larger than the petals, and the other segments of the flower are frequently borne inside of these connected or fused portions. The blossoms occur in every color imaginable, though green and brown are perhaps the most frequent hues. Many of the species are noted for the strange or foetid scents given off by the flowers.

CULTURE: Because of the prodigious size of this genus, a definite set of cultural requirements would be almost impossible to give. In general, however, they should be grown as are Dendrobiums, preferably in shallow fern-pans or baskets, so that the generally elongate rhizomes will have sufficient room for expansion. The majority of species should be kept in a warm, humid situation and given a short rest-period upon completion of the new growths. The ultra-tropical types, such as those from low elevations in Southeast Asia, Indonesia, and New Guinea, must be kept constantly hot and never permitted to become dry. (I,H)

B. barbigerum (bar-*bij*-er-um)   (Tropical West Africa)

Dwarf, creeping epiphyte. Pbs. 1″ in diameter, compressed. Lf. solitary, leathery, to 4″ long. Infl. to 10″ tall, bearing up to 15 fls. about 1″ long, these rather foul-smelling. Ss. and ps. small, greenish brown. Lip proportionately very large, yellowish, furnished on the sides with twin tufts of brown-purple hairs, which oscillate with every slight breeze. Summer. (H)

B. falcatum (fal-*kah*-tum)   (Tropical West Africa)

Pbs. rather close together, to 3″ tall, with a pair of leathery apical leaves. Infls. to 8″ tall, usually arching, the rachis flattened into a paddle-shaped structure. (This is typical of this section, *Megaclinium*, which is sometimes treated as a genus distinct from *Bulbophyllum*.) Flowers about ¼–½″ long, produced from the flattened sides of the rachis, very intricate, yellowish brown marked with purple. Lip mostly dark purple, mobile. Spring–early summer. (H)

Bulbophyllum falcatum

B. Lobbii (*lob*-ee-eye) (Burma; Indonesia)

Medium-sized for the genus. Pbs. glossy, egg-shaped, to 3″ tall, 1-leaved. Lvs. to 10″ long, rigidly erect, leathery, somewhat stalked basally. Fls. solitary, borne on tall erect stems, to 5″ across, fragrant, very handsome. Ss. and ps. usually buff-yellow, more or less marked with purple or brown-purple, this color mostly more prominent on reverse. Lip highly mobile, brown. A variable species, one of the finest in the genus. Summer. (I,H)

B. Medusae (med-*oo*-see) (Malaya; Indonesia)

Rather small, curious-looking, creeping epiphyte. Pbs. about 1½″ tall, borne at intervals along the rhiz., 1-lvd. Lvs. leathery, to 7″ long and 1½″ broad. Infls. usually somewhat arching, to 6″ tall, bearing a dense moplike head of fragrant fls. at apex. Fls. pale straw- or cream-yellow, more or less spotted or dotted with reddish or red-purple on all parts. Lateral sepals elongated into threadlike segments to 6″ long, other parts elongated, but less so. Summer. (I,H)

CALANTHE
(kah-*lan*-thee)

The genus *Calanthe* includes almost 150 species of mostly terrestrial orchids which are native in an area extending from South Africa and Madagascar throughout Tropical Asia to New Guinea and the Fiji Islands, with a single representative in the West Indies and Central America. These fine orchids, closely allied to *Phaius*, are frequently found in collections today because of their showy flowers and easy cultivation. The genus is horticulturally (and culturally) divided into two well marked sections, one with prominent pseudobulbs and deciduous, folded foliage, the other with obscure bulbs and persistent leaves. The flowers, which have a lobed lip generally much larger than the spreading sepals and petals, are mostly rather soft-textured, highly variable in color, and numerous at the top of an erect or arching inflorescence.

CULTURE: Calanthes should be treated in two ways, depending upon the vegetative appearance of the species or hybrid. The evergreen, non-pseudobulbous plants require conditions such as those given *Phaius* (see page 199). The deciduous, pseudobulbous species should be grown in a slightly richer compost than the others, with the addition of some sphagnum and gritty clean sand, and with copious crock to assure perfect drainage scattered through the planting medium. Fertilizer should be applied liberally while the growths are maturing. The foliage falls when the pseudobulbs are ripe and the inflorescence appears; water should be considerably reduced at this time. After flowering, the bulbs should be removed from the pot—in most cases, separated—and stored on their sides, bare-root, in a dry cool place until the new shoots are about 2″ long, then replanted. Calanthes of this section in general require division and repotting on an annual basis. They delight in a rather sunny location in a warm greenhouse. (I,H)

C. rosea (*row*-zee-ah) (Burma)

Deciduous. Pbs. spindle-shaped, to 7″ tall, swollen basally, with terminal ribbed lvs. of flaccid texture. Scapes basal, nodding, to 3′ tall, many-fld. Fls. about 3″ long, lasting well, varying in color from pale rose-pink to white or dark rose. Lip flattish, with white or whitish lat. lbs. Winter. (I)

C. veratrifolia (ver-at-ri-*foe*-lee-ah) (Indonesia, Australia)

Evergreen species, variable. Lvs. large, folded, light green, numerous, to more than 3′ tall. Scapes to 5′ tall, often several from one growth, many-fld., erect. Fls. usually about 2″ long, white, long-lasting. Lip usually with a vivid yellow splotch in the center and a deeply cut midlobe. Summer. (H)

C. vestita (*vess*-ti-tah)   (Burma, Thailand)

Deciduous, variable. Pbs. large, egg-shaped, somewhat 4-angled, covered with silvery-gray sheaths. Lvs. large, folded, falling before the

Calanthe vestita var. *rubro-oculata*

fls. are produced. Scapes to 5′ long, usually gracefully arched, few- to many-fld. Fls. about 2″ long, white or cream-white, with a blotch at the lip-base which varies from light yellow to vivid red. A popular species. Late fall–winter. (I)

CATASETUM
(kat-ah-*see*-tum)

This is a group of about 110 species of epiphytic, lithophytic, or rarely semiterrestrial orchids in the American tropics, reaching their greatest development in Brazil. They are characterized by fleshy, cylindrical, or globose pseudobulbs, folded, eventually deciduous leaves, and usually elongate racemes of small to rather large waxy flowers which differ in sex. The various sex forms—male, female, and hermaphrodite

—vary radically in form and color, a characteristic resulting in a confused and extensive synonymy in the genus, since the same plant may have been described under different names simply because of the diversity exhibited by the three sex forms of the flowers. Though the male (staminate) flowers are generally distinctive in each species, the female (pistillate) blossoms are much alike in many species, and thus cause great confusion. The flowers are greenish, white, yellow, brown, or red, often spotted and barred, and are typically of extremely complex and unusual construction.

CULTURE: These strange orchids are best grown in baskets or well-drained pots in warm, humid situation; they are highly susceptible to over-watering, and the fleshy pseudobulbs are prone to rot if the compost is allowed to become stale or sour. An ideal compost is tightly packed osmunda fiber or smallish chunks of tree-fern fiber. When the growths have matured, the plants should be permitted a definite rest-period. Catasetums delight in a sunny location, particularly after the leaves have fallen from the mature pseudobulbs. (I,H)

C. fimbriatum (fim-bree-*ah*-tum)   (Brazil; Paraguay; Uruguay)

Robust species, the pbs. somewhat spindle-shaped, to 1′ tall, usually tinged with dull red. Lvs. several, deciduous, folded, to 1′ long. Infls. arching, bearing about 12–15 fls. about 2½″ across. Ss. and ps. green, tinged and spotted with red-brown, the dorsal sep. and ps. turned upward and somewhat reflexed. Lip saclike, deeply fringed, white with some yellowish in the middle. Mostly summer. (I,H)

C. macrocarpum (mak-row-*kar*-pum)   (South America)

A large, variable orchid of wide range. Pbs. thick, to 8″ tall, somewhat cylindrical. Lvs. as in *C. fimbriatum*. Infls. usually multiple, erect, bearing up to 15 fls. Fls. hooded, fragrant, waxy, to more than 3″ long, green or greenish yellow, sometimes more or less red-spotted. Lip usually yellow, saclike, very fleshy, on top of flower. Summer or at various seasons. (H)

C. viridiflavum (vi-ri-dee-*flah*-vum)   (Panama)

Pbs. to 10″ tall, fleshy, often rather irregularly formed. Lvs. large, numerous for the genus. Infls. mostly erect, to more than 2′ tall, several-fld. Fls. about 3½″ long, showy, fragrant, greenish but turning to dull yellow with age. Lip hood-shaped, uppermost, very fleshy, yellow and apple-green, often flushed inside with pale orange. Spring–summer. (I,H)

Catasetum macrocarpum

H. TEUSCHER

CATTLEYA
(*kat*-lee-yah)

To the public, Cattleyas are certainly the best known of all orchidaceous plants, and, with their innumerable allied genera and hybrid groups, are the ones most frequently encountered in collections. About 65 species of epiphytic, lithophytic, or very rarely terrestrial members comprise the genus, which is distributed from Mexico to Bolivia, Paraguay, and Argentina, with centers of development being found in the Andes and in Brazil. The flowers are among the most magnificent of any found in the family, and are so well known that a description is certainly superfluous here. They vary considerably in color—often within a single species or variant—but are of rather characteristic formation, generally bearing a tubular lip and spreading enlarged sepals and petals, thus forming a blossom of startling beauty and often of huge dimensions. The plants are likewise diversified, with pseudobulbs of varying lengths and thicknesses, frequently being somewhat club-shaped and bearing one or two heavily leathery apical leaves. The flowers, with very few exceptions, are produced from the top of the pseudobulb, singly or in few-flowered racemes. There are many thousands of hybrids within this genus, and as many crosses between *Cattleya* and certain of its allied groups.

CULTURE: Cattleyas are among the orchids that are easy to grow. Indoors they will thrive in pots or baskets; in warm climates, they can be grown on trees or rocks or even in outdoor beds filled with suitable compost. A potting medium of straight, firmly packed osmunda is generally used, with liberal quantities of broken crock in the bottom of the container for proper drainage. The plants should be repotted (and divided, if necessary) whenever they are about to outgrow their containers, usually about every other year. Freely moving air should always be made available, as well as copious water and a humid atmosphere when the plants are in active growth. Upon maturation of the new pseudobulbs, water should be given in lesser quantities, but care must be taken not to permit any shriveling of either these bulbs or of the foliage. Most of the species and hybrids delight in almost full sun. Though the plants will become yellowish in color, large numbers of the magnificent flowers will then be produced. Included in this category are several of the *C. labiata* variations, such as var. *Dowiana* and its subvar. *aurea,* and var. *Warscewiczii,* and most of the long-bulbed, bifoliate species. All Cattleyas benefit materially by frequent and rather liberal applications of fertilizing solutions. (I,H)

C. bicolor (bye-*kol*-or) (Brazil)

Pbs. stiff, erect, stemlike, to 3′ tall, 2-leaved. Lvs. to 6″ long, thick and rigid. Fls. solitary to few, long-lived, fragrant, about 4½″ across, very thick and waxy, mostly bronze-green. Lip dark magenta, usually with white edges, without lateral lobes, thus giving rise to the "isthmus" lip in its hybrid progeny. Fall. (I,H)

C. Bowringiana (bow-ring-ee-*ah*-nah) (British Honduras)

Pbs. stem-like, with a very prominent bulbous thickening at base, to 3′ tall. Leaves 2–4, thickly leathery, bluish green in many specimens. Infl. to about 8″ tall, densely many-fld., the individual fls. about 3″ across, odorless. Ss. and ps. rose-magenta or pale rose. Lip tubular at base, golden-yellow in the throat, the spreading midlobe somewhat darker colored than the other parts. Late fall–winter. (I,H)

C. guttata (goo-*tah*-tah) (Brazil)

Highly variable in color and stature. Pbs. stemlike, often red-tinted, to as much as 4½′ tall, with two rather small rigidly leathery apical lvs. Fls. up to 30 per spike (often considerably fewer), to 4″ across, very waxen and stiff in texture, highly fragrant. Ss. and ps. typically green or yellow-green, spotted or blotched with brownish red, lacquered.

Lip mostly rose-red or white, the midlobe usually white dotted with magenta. Fall–winter. (I,H)

C. intermedia (in-ter-*mee*-dee-ah) (Brazil)

Pbs. stemlike, bifoliate, to 1½′ tall in robust phases. Fls. 3–8 in number, to 5″ across, with pale blush-rose ss. and ps. Lip whitish with very dark magenta-rose markings on the midlb. and some yellow in the throat. Forma *alba* is an extremely rare variant with magnificent waxen pure-white fls. Summer. (I,H)

C. labiata (lah-bee-*ah*-tah) (Brazil)

Typical of the single-leafed (unifoliate or monophyllous) section of the genus. Pbs. club-shaped, to about 12″ tall, generally much shorter. Lf. solitary, very thickly leathery, usually longer than the pbs. Fls. up to 5 per infl., fragrant, highly variable in color, to 5″ across. Ss. and ps. typically bright rose, crisped marginally. Lip dark crimson-magenta, very frilled, with a large yellow mark in the tubular throat. Mostly fall–early winter. (I,H)

Most members of the so-called "*labiata*" group of *Cattleya* are treated by orchid growers as species, but technically they are only variants of *C. labiata* itself. Those most frequently grown variants are:

—var. Dowiana (dow-ee-*ah*-nah) (Costa Rica)

Similar in habit to the species, often larger. Fls. 2–3, very fragrant, to 8″ across. Ss. and ps. Nankeen-yellow, marked and suffused with

H. A. DUNN   H. A. DUNN

Cattleya labiata var. *Dowiana*   *Cattleya labiata* var. *Trianaei*

crimson-magenta, very crisped. Lip large, rich crimson-magenta, streaked and veined with brilliant gold. The subvar. *aurea* from Colombia, has a more richly colored lip, and is more common in collections than the Costa Rican plant. Late summer–fall. (I)

—var. **Gaskelliana** (gas-kel-ee-*ah*-nah) (Venezuela)

Similar to the species, but with generally smaller fls. (usually less than 5″ across), colored much like the var. *Mossiae*, but without the prominent orange or yellow streaking on the purple portion of the lip's midlb. Highly variable, and often difficult to determine. Spring. (I,H)

—var. **Lueddemanniana** (loo-ed-e-man-ee-*ah*-nah) (Venezuela)

A very large-flowered variant, at times to 9″ across. Ss. and ps. usually pale blush-white to light rose, the large lip with a rather flattened tube, the spreading midlb. magenta, intricately veined and flushed with whitish yellow. Summer. (I,H)

—var. **Mossiae** (*moss*-ee-eye) (Venezuela)

Similar in habit to the species, but highly variable. Fls. to 8″ across, fragrant. Ss. and ps. usually light rose. Lip crimson with a rather orange throat, into which extend some dark magenta-purple markings from the midlb., which is irregularly veined and spotted with orange or yellow. Spring–early summer. (I,H)

—var. **Percivaliana** (per-si-val-ee-*ah*-nah) (Venezuela)

Rather similar to var. *Mossiae*, with fls. usually about 4″ across, musk-scented. Lip very dark magenta-purple on midlb., with a cinnamon-brown-purple blotch at the entrance to the yellow-orange throat. Winter–early spring. (I,H)

—var. **Trianaei** (tree-*ah*-nee-eye) (Colombia)

Similar in habit to the species, often somewhat larger. Fls. to 9″ across, highly variable, fragrant. Ss. and ps. mostly blush-rose. Lip crimson-magenta, with an orange throat, the dark purple-magenta area on the midlb. rather sharply delimited. Winter. (I,H)

—var. **Warscewiczii** (var-she-*vich*-ee-eye) (Colombia)

Similar to the species, usually more robust. Fls. to 11″ across, variable in color. Ss. and ps. generally dark rose. Lip very large, dark lustrous crimson-magenta with two prominent white or yellowish blotches near the tubular throat. Spring. (I,H)

C. Skinneri (*skin*-er-eye)   (Mexico, Central America)

Similar in habit to *C. Bowringiana,* but usually smaller and with no basal bulbous thickening on the pbs. Fls. 2–6 in number, about 3″ across, odorless, the ss. and ps. mostly rather dark rose-magenta. Lip tubular, the throat with a white blotch, the spreading midlb. somewhat darker. Spring–summer. (I,H)

CATTLEYOPSIS
(kat-lee-*op*-siss)

This is a genus of three species of handsome bright-flowered epiphytic or lithophytic orchids in the Antillean region, now becoming rather popular with collectors. *Cattleyopsis* is closely allied to *Broughtonia,* with which its members are sometimes confused. The dwarf plants give rise to elongate racemes of very showy smallish flowers, which simulate a *Cattleya* in shape, hence the generic name, which means "*Cattleya*-like."

CULTURE: As for *Broughtonia.* (H)

C. Lindeni (*lin*-den-eye)   (Bahamas, Cuba)

Pbs. small, ringed, gray-green. Lvs. paired, rigid, thick, gray-green, about 5″ long, toothed on the margins. Infls. to 3′ long, arching, with up to 12 fls. at the apex. Fls. rather fragile, to 2″ across, pale blush-rose. Lip large, vivid rose, with complex wavy crimson lines and a yellowish throat. Late winter–spring. (H)

C. Ortgiesiana (ort-gee-see-*ah*-nah)   (Bahamas, Cuba)

Similar to the other species, but smaller. Infl. to 3½′ long, many-fld. Fls. about 1″ across or slightly more, vivid rose-magenta, the lip darker, marked with more intense purple-magenta and bright yellow, long-lasting, very handsome, almost round and very flattened. Late winter–spring. (H)

CHONDRORHYNCHA
(kond-ror-*ing*-kah)

This is a complex genus of about 12 species, now including *Warscewiczella.* Epiphytic plants, mostly inhabitants of the chill "cloud forests" from Mexico to Brazil, they are but rarely encountered in our

Cattleya Skinneri fma. *alba*

Cattleya x Ville de Liege var. *alba*

collections at this time. The plants consist of rather fragile leaves arranged in the shape of a loose fan, from the base of which the solitary flowers are produced. These blossoms, often multiple per growth, are of complex structure and handsome appearance.

CULTURE: As for *Huntleya*. (C,I)

C. discolor (*dis*-kol-or)   (Cuba, Costa Rica, Panama)

Lvs. rather pale green and thin-textured, to 2′ long and 2″ broad, narrow. Scapes usually several from base of each new growth, nodding,

Chondrorhyncha marginata

DRAWING BY DOROTHY O. ALLEN

to 5″ long. Fls. about 3″ across, strongly fragrant, waxy, long-lasting. Ss. white, the ps. thrust forward, white flushed with violet or purple. Lip very dark violet-purple to almost blue-purple, the callus large, complex, white. Late spring–fall. (I)

CHYSIS
(*kye*-siss)

Chysis consists of a few epiphytic, mostly pendulous, showy orchids in Mexico, Central America, and northern South America, today infrequent in cultivation. The pseudobulbs are fleshy, strongly club-shaped, and bear several folded leaves which generally drop before the flowers appear. The waxy, aromatic blossoms, which are borne in short racemes, appear concurrently with the new growths and last a long time. The fleshy sepals and petals are somewhat cup-shaped, while the lip is excavated and ridged and often of a different color.

CULTURE: Chysis should be grown in slatted baskets tilted on their sides (so that the pseudobulbs may hang in the normal pendent manner), tightly packed with osmunda fiber. A bright sunny situation is required for proper flowering, and while the plants are actively growing water should be given in large amounts. Upon maturation of the pseudobulbs, the plants should be placed in a somewhat cooler spot and watering lessened. When the new growths start to appear, removal to a warmer location and increased moisture are needed. These fine orchids benefit by regular fertilizing. Frequent repotting is to be avoided. (I)

C. aurea (aw-*ree*-ah)   (Mexico to Venezuela and Peru)

Pbs. club-shaped, pendulous, to about 1′ long. Lvs. folded, light green, deciduous. Infls. with up to 8 fls., arising with new growths.

Chysis aurea

P. H. ALLEN

Fls. fragrant, waxy, to 3″ across. Ss. and ps. tawny yellow, often marked and spotted with blood-red. Lip very fleshy, mostly blood-red. Mostly in spring. (I)

C. bractescens (brak-*tess*-enz)   (Mexico; Guatemala)

Habit as in *C. aurea*, but larger in all parts. Infls. with 10–12 handsome, powerfully scented fls. about 3″ across. Ss. and ps. waxy, pure white or cream. Lip yellow in the center, sometimes with sparse red markings. Spring. (I)

C. laevis (*lie*-viss)   (Mexico to Costa Rica)

Habit as in *C. aurea*, but much larger vegetatively. Infls. pendulous or arching, with 8–12 fragrant, long-lasting fls. about 2½–3″ across. Ss. and ps. waxy, brilliant orange-yellow. Lip fringed marginally, marked more or less heavily with blood-red. Summer. (I)

COCHLIODA
(kok-lee-*oh*-dah)

Five species of *Cochlioda* are known, all attractive epiphytic or lithophytic plants from the high mountains of Colombia, Ecuador, and Peru. They are occasionally seen in choice collections, and are particularly noteworthy for their use in hybridization, being utilized to impart their fiery scarlet-red coloration to the allied groups *Oncidium*, *Miltonia*, and *Odontoglossum* (yielding *Oncidioda*, *Miltonioda*, and *Odontioda*, respectively). In habit the plants resemble the Odontoglossums, and the magnificent red blossoms are produced in dense arching racemes of extraordinary beauty.

CULTURE: As for the alpine Odontoglossums. (C)

C. Noetzliana (netz-lee-*ah*-nah)   (Peru)

Pbs. smooth, egg-shaped, clustered, to 2″ tall. Lvs. leathery, to 1′ long. Infls. racemose, arching gracefully, many-fld., to 1½′ long. Fls. opening widely, about 2½″ across, vivid scarlet-red, the lip somewhat darker. Fall. (C)

COELOGYNE
(seh-*law*-ji-nee)

This is a genus of upwards of 150 species, mostly epiphytes, widespread in the Asiatic tropics from China to New Guinea and the Fiji Islands. *Coelogyne* is a popular group in orchid collections, with several particularly handsome hybrids being on record. The plants are highly variable in habit, but usually have rather slender pseudobulbs on a more or less creeping rhizome, bearing one or a pair of leathery apical leaves, and producing erect or sharply pendulous inflorescences, which generally arise from the center of the new growth. The flowers, often produced in large numbers, are rather waxy in texture, and occur mostly in white or in shades of brown, yellow, or green. They are frequently very fragrant, and last for a long period. The most common of the so-called "Black Orchids" belongs to this genus—*Coelogyne pandurata*.

CULTURE: From a cultural standpoint, this genus is divided into two major groups: the montane or high-elevation species, which should be treated much like the alpine Odontoglossums, and the low-elevation types. The latter are best accommodated in baskets, which allow room for their often rampant rhizomes, in a rather tightly-packed compost of osmunda fiber, with liberal crock interspersed for perfect drainage. These Coelogynes require a hot or at least warm, humid location, without any protracted rest-period, and should not be subjected to full sun-exposure at any time. Care must be taken that no water is allowed to lodge within the new growths (which ordinarily have the immature inflorescences inside them), or rotting may result. (C,I,H)

C. cristata (kris-*tah*-tah) (Himalayas; Burma)

Cool-growing species. Pbs. almost globular, clustered, light apple-green, to 4″ tall, 2-leaved. Lvs. to 10″ long, rather flaccid. Infls. drooping or arching, bearing up to 10 fragrant and beautiful fls., each about 4″ across. Ss. and ps. pure white. Lip large, waxy, white, marked with prominent golden-yellow keels. Winter–early spring. (C)

C. Dayana (day-*ah*-nah) (Malaya; Indonesia)

Hot-growing species. Pbs. conical, to about 8″ tall, with 2 or 3 large leathery lvs. Infls. sharply pendulous, to 4′ long, with 50–80 fragrant fls. about 2″ across, long-lived. Ss. and ps. ochre-yellow. Lip whitish, striped and margined with dark chocolate-brown, the prominent keels darker. Spring–early summer. (H)

C. Huettneriana (hoo-et-ner-ee-*ah*-nah) (Burma; Thailand)

Hot- or intermediate-growing species. Pbs. vaguely angular, dark green, to 4″ tall, with 2 lvs. about 9″ long. Infls. arching, with 12 or more 2″ fls. which are very fragrant and long-lived. Ss. and ps. pure glittering white. Lip marked more or less with brownish-red, the center vivid yellow. Summer–fall. (I,H)

C. pandurata (pan-doo-*rah*-tah)   (Sumatra, Borneo, Malay Peninsula)

Hot-growing species. Pbs. rather compressed on both sides, smooth, borne at intervals from one another, to 7″ tall and 4″ broad, with 2 large leathery lvs. Infls. arching, to 2′ long, with up to 20 fls., each about 4″ across, heavy-textured, highly fragrant, and handsome. Ss. and ps. apple-green. Lip large, intricate, white mottled and marked with brown-black. Fall. (H)

Coelogyne Dayana

J. E. DOWNWARD

COMPARETTIA
(kom-pah-*ret*-ee-ah)

The genus *Comparettia* consists of about a dozen species, native over a large area extending from Cuba and Mexico to the South American Andes. It is a peculiar group, as yet very scarce in our collections. The typically epiphytic plants are without prominent pseudobulbs, but have relatively large fleshy leaves and erect to pendulous sprays of showy flowers, generally of vivid scarlet or crimson, and frequently of proportionately large size.

CULTURE: As for *Ornithocephalus*. (I)

C. falcata (fal-*kah*-tah)   (Mexico to Peru)

Pbs. diminutive. Lvs. broad and fleshy, often strongly suffused with wine-purple, to about 4″ long. Infls. erect or arching, few-fld., the fls. usually opening successively over a long period. Fls. about 1¼″ long, lasting well, the ss. and ps. usually vivid magenta-rose. Lip large, somewhat darker, with a purple-red median part. Winter or at various seasons. (I)

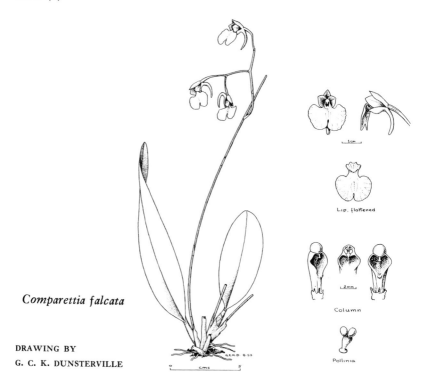

Comparettia falcata

DRAWING BY
G. C. K. DUNSTERVILLE

CORYANTHES
(ko-ree-*an*-theez)

Coryanthes contains some 15 species of epiphytic orchids in the American tropics, related to *Stanhopea* and approximating that genus in general vegetative habit, but bearing very large flowers which are probably unexcelled in the entire Orchidaceae for weird complexity of structure. The blossoms are borne on slim pendulous (very rarely erect) racemes arising from the pseudobulb-bases, and are typically few in number, fleshy, and usually give off a penetrating aromatic odor. Colors in the genus are mostly cream or green, often spotted with lurid combinations of reds and purples. The lip is of an incredibly complicated design, bearing a cup-like section which is filled with a liquid exuded by glands at the base of the column, and the entire flower is constructed in a most extraordinary fashion. As yet very rare in cultivation, this is one of the most fascinating of all orchid groups. The species are commonly known as "Bucket Orchids," because of the saclike lip structure.

CULTURE: The culture of *Coryanthes* is basically that recommended for *Stanhopea* (see page 219), except that all of the species require a uniformly warm, humid atmosphere at all times. Because of the strongly pendent nature of the inflorescences in all save two of the species (neither of these appears to be in cultivation at this time), the plants must be grown in open-slatted baskets. (I,H)

C. macrantha (mak-*ran*-thah)   (Venezuela to Brazil and Peru)

Pbs. ribbed, elongate-egg-shaped, usually single-leaved, about 3″ tall. Lf. stalked, folded, dull green. Infls. pendulous, elongate, wirelike, usually 1-fld. Fls. to as much as 6″ across, fleshy, short-lived, fragrant. Ss. and ps. dull yellow, spotted and blotched with dull purple. Lip extremely complex, variously green, greenish-violet, and blood-red, with the large "bucket" vivid yellow marked with crimson. Summer. (H)

C. speciosa (spee-see-*oh*-sah)   (Guatemala to Trinidad and Brazil)

Habit as in *C. macrantha*, but somewhat more robust and the infls. bearing up to 6 fls., these almost 8″ across, fragrant, not lasting well. Ss. and ps. mostly yellow-brown, sometimes spotted with dark brown. Lip orange-yellow, the "bucket" yellow-red. Summer. (I,H)

CRYPTOPHORANTHUS
(krip-toe-foe-*ran*-thuss)

This is an amazing genus, comprising perhaps 20 species, native from Cuba and Jamaica to Brazil. They are mostly dwarf epiphytes, belonging to the subtribe *Pleurothallidinae*, being allied to *Masdevallia* and *Pleurothallis*. The typically solitary flowers, purple, red, or brownish in color, are among the most unusual of any found in the Orchidaceae, the large sepals being joined together at the tops and opening only along two tiny slits at the sides, through which pollinating insects may enter. It is from this unique characteristic that they obtain their common name of "Window Orchids."

CULTURE: The cultural requirements of *Cryptophoranthus* are those of other delicate epiphytic orchids, such as *Ornithocephalus* (see page 194). They prefer pot-culture, in straight osmunda, and since no moisture-storing structures are present, must never be allowed to be-

Flora Brasílica

Coryanthes speciosa

come dry. A warm, relatively shaded spot in the greenhouse serves them well. Frequent repotting should be avoided. (I,H)

C. atropurpureus (at-row-pur-*pur*-ee-us)   (Cuba; Jamaica)

To about 6″ tall, clustered. Sts. slender, about 3½″ tall, with a solitary, fleshy, paddle-shaped lf. at the top. Fls. solitary but multiple at lf.-base, 2–4 in number, usually opening in succession, rather foul-smelling, short-lived, about ½″ long, dark dull purple or dark crimson-red, often spotted or mottled with darker color. Fall. (I)

Cryptophoranthus atropurpureus

F. C. HOEHNE

CYCNOCHES
(*sik*-noe-keez)

Eleven species and varieties make up the fascinating genus *Cycnoches*, the common name of which is "Swan Orchids," because of the long curving column that simulates the gracefully arching neck of a swan. They are all robust epiphytic orchids, native from Mexico to Brazil. Flowers of different sexes—male, female, and hermaphroditic forms—are produced at different times (rarely simultaneously) on the same plant. The elongate pseudobulbs are usually cylindrical and fleshy. The large folded leaves, which are quickly deciduous, and also the flower-stalks arise from the top of the bulb. The flowers are generally few and large or numerous and small on long racemes. These blossoms are fleshy, aromatic, and rather long-lived. They differ widely in size and structure in the various sexual forms, and vary in color from yellow or green spotted with brown to clear golden-yellow or apple-green.

CULTURE: The cultural requirements of *Cycnoches* are those given to *Catasetum*, to which they are rather closely allied. They require a high temperature and moist atmosphere, but care must be taken not to overwater them during the time of active growth, as the pseudo-bulbs are prone to rot. They are best grown in well-drained pots, and require a strict rest of about two weeks' duration upon completion of the new growths. (I,H)

C. Egertonianum (ej-er-tow-nee-*ah*-num) (Mexico to Peru and Brazil)

Highly variable, the general habit as noted for the genus. Staminate (male) fls. produced in many-fld. racs. to several feet long, fragrant, to

Cycnoches Egertonianum var. *Dianae*

H. A. DUNN

2″ across, green or greenish tan sometimes spotted with red-brown, maroon or purple. Lip green to pure white, with numerous toothlike marginal projections. Pistillate (female) fls. very rarely produced, few in number, larger than the males, very fleshy, green or yellow-green. Summer. (I,H)

C. ventricosum var. **Warscewiczii** (ven-tri-*koe*-sum
var-she-*vich*-ee-eye) (Costa Rica; Panama)

The species itself is extremely rare in cultivation, and this commonly seen variant is usually grown under the incorrect name of *Cycnoches chlorochilon*. Pbs. to 3′ tall, cylindrical, stout, gray-green and wrinkled with age. Lvs. deciduous, to 2′ long, folded, rather narrow. Infls. most from near pb.-tops, with a few heavy-textured, fragrant fls. to 5″ across. Ss. and ps. yellowish green to almost yellow. Lip large, fleshy, white, the basal callus very thick, almost black-green. Summer. (I,H)

CYMBIDIUM
(sim-*bid*-ee-um)

Cymbidium is made up of about 70 species of variously terrestrial, lithophytic, or epiphytic plants in the Asiatic tropics and subtropics and the nearby insular areas. In their almost numberless hybrid forms, Cymbidiums are widely utilized for commercial purposes. The plants typically have short robust pseudobulbs and long ribbon-shaped leathery leaves. They bear either erect or pendulous racemes of small to very large, heavy-textured flowers. These blossoms are highly variable, and are found in a multitude of hues from white or yellow to dark purple-maroon. The members of this genus are among the most popular and widely cultivated of all orchids, with even an international Cymbidium Society being devoted to their study.

CULTURE: The majority of the Cymbidiums in cultivation are terrestrial or semiepiphytic in habit, and should be grown accordingly. With the notable exception of the *C. Finlaysonianum* group (all of which are epiphytic or lithophytic, and should be grown in baskets tightly packed with osmunda fiber) they take particularly well to pot culture, preferring a certain amount of pot-binding for proper production of the majestic flowers. The pots should be filled with a mixture of chopped osmunda, sphagnum moss, and rich leafy humus, with copious broken crock in the bottom to assure perfect drainage. They delight in a relatively moist atmosphere while in active growth, but watering should be curtailed when the spikes are being produced. Most of the species under cultivation, also the artificial hybrids—of which there are several thousand on record—should be kept in a relatively cool spot, with not too much direct sunlight, or burning of the foliage may result. Since these orchids are very heavy feeders, they should be fertilized frequently and liberally. (C,I,H)

C. eburneum (ee-*bur*-nee-um)   (India; Himalayas)

Pbs. rather rounded, clustered, about 3″ tall, furrowed in age. Lvs. dark glossy green, to 2′ long, arching, numerous. Infls. mostly stiffly erect, with 2 or more fls. which are very fragrant, waxy, and long-lived. Fls. to 3" across, white or cream-white. Lip white with a dark orange-yellow median disc. Mostly late winter. (C,I)

C. Finlaysonianum (fin-lay-son-ee-*ah*-num)
(Malaya; Indonesia; Philippines)

Pbs. negligible. Lvs. erect or arching, mostly yellowish green, to 3' long, very thick and leathery, bilobed at tip. Infls. to 5' long, sharply pendulous, set with rather triangular, numerous fls. about 2½" across. Ss. and ps. narrow, fleshy, dark red or maroon-red in the middle, with yellowish margins. Lip dark maroon-red, with dull white and yellow streaks in the middle. Summer. (I,H)

C. Lowianum (low-ee-*ah*-num) (Burma; India)

Pbs. rather globular, clustered, about 3" tall. Lvs. ribbon-shaped, dark green, to 3' long, mostly arching. Infls. basal, gracefully arching, to 4½' long, with up to 30 spectacular fls. Fls. to 5" across, waxy, handsome, and long-lived. Ss. and ps. yellow-green or chartreuse, somewhat suffused and streaked with greenish brown. Lip creamy white, with the apical margin dark dull red. A highly variable plant, and one of the most popular species. Spring. (C,I)

CYPRIPEDIUM
(sip-ri-*pee*-dee-um)

This is a genus of some 50 species of terrestrial orchids, found in virtually all of the temperate and subtropical regions of the globe. Known commonly as "Lady's-Slippers" or "Moccasin Flowers," they are characterized by showy flowers, mostly pink, green, brownish, yellow, or white in color, with a prominent pouch-like lip and two fertile anthers instead of the single one found in almost all other orchids. The blossoms are single or multiple, borne above the generally ample, folded foliage. This name *Cypripedium* is often erroneously and confusingly applied to members of the tropical genus *Paphiopedilum* (which see).

CULTURE: Cypripediums should be grown in well-drained pots of humus, liberally mixed with chopped sphagnum moss and chopped osmunda fiber, given abundant water while growing, and a decided and protracted rest-period when the new growths are matured. A rather cool but sunny situation is required for success. They also grow well when cultivated in outdoor beds, along with other herbaceous plants. (C,I)

Cymbidium x Jungfrau var. *Snow Queen*

Cymbidium x Water Rail var. *Dubloon*

C. parviflorum (par-vi-*flo*-rum)   (North America)

Lvs. several, rather large, bright glossy green. Spikes to about 1′ tall, with one or two fls. almost 5″ across. Ss. and ps. variable in color, from dark lustrous crimson-purple to greenish-yellow, the ps. strongly spiraled and out-stretched. Lip inflated, egg-shaped, shiny golden-yellow. Late spring–fall. (C,I)

C. reginae (reh-*jee*-nee)   (North America)

To about 3′ tall, with several folded fuzzy lvs. to 7″ long. Fls. short-stalked, 1–4 in number, to 3½″ across, fragrant and very beautiful. Ss.

Cypripedium reginae

and ps. pure white, not twisted. Lip very inflated, almost globular, about 1½″ long, white flushed and mottled with green and vivid rose-purple. This is the State Flower of Minnesota. Summer. (C,I)

CYRTOPODIUM
(seer-toe-*poe*-dee-um)

About 35 species of mostly robust epiphytic, lithophytic, or terrestrial orchids make up the genus *Cyrtopodium*, members of which are widely distributed in Tropical America from Florida southward, with the largest development in Brazil. Typically the members of this group have very large club-shaped pseudobulbs bearing numerous deciduous folded leaves and erect basal inflorescences of considerable size, which produce a great many spectacular flowers—mostly yellow, red, or brown in color—among leafy bracts of similar coloration. Cyrtopodiums are unfortunately little known in cultivation at this time, but their ease of growth and remarkable appearance make them among the most satisfactory of all large orchids for the amateur hobbyist.

CULTURE: The cultural requirements of these plants are in the main those suggested for *Cymbidium*, since they prefer a very rich, earthy compost (the humus content of the pots should be cut down somewhat in such species as *C. punctatum*), copious water, heat and heavy fertilizer while growing, and a decided rest of upwards of one month upon completion of the new growths. The inflorescences in most species arise side-by-side with the new shoots. Most of the Cyrtopodiums in cultivation will not flower readily unless they are subjected to almost full sunshine at all times. (I,H)

C. Andersoni (*an*-der-son-eye)   (West Indies, N. South America)

Robust and variable. Pbs. spindle-shaped to almost cylindrical, mostly yellowish, nodes very prominent, to 5′ tall and 4″ in diameter. Lvs. proportionately small, pale yellowish green, deciduous. Infl. a branching panicle to 6′ tall, bearing many 1½″ fragrant waxy fls. which are notably long-lived. Ss. and ps. lemon-yellow, somewhat tinged with pale green. Lip dark yellow, sometimes almost orange-yellow. Spring–summer. (I,H)

C. punctatum (punk-*tah*-tum)   (South Florida to Brazil)

Widespread, variable, similar to *C. Andersoni* in habit, though not as robust, the pbs. more cylindrical and the lvs. longer. Infl. usually less than 4′ tall, profusely branched, with as many as 200 fls. Fls. about 2″ across, long-lasting, fragrant, each one subtended by a rather large wavy bract that, like the ss. and ps., is colored chartreuse, spotted and blotched with dark dull red, the ps., however, mostly yellowish with only a few spots toward the base. Lip mostly dark brown-red, the middle bright yellow, the grooved crest yellow spotted with red. Late winter–spring. (I,H)

Cyrtopodium punctatum

DENDROBIUM
(den-*droe*-bee-um)

This is among the largest of all orchid genera, with in excess of 1500 species widely distributed in the Asiatic tropics and adjacent insular areas, eastward to the Fiji Islands. Many of the Dendrobiums are extremely popular with orchidists, because of the handsome flowers, which are usually produced in very large numbers. This genus is divided into numerous smaller sections, which vary greatly in habit, so that it is difficult to describe a "typical" member of *Dendrobium*. Generally the plants possess thickened pseudobulbs bearing alternate, more or less succulent leaves, which are rather frequently deciduous, and either racemes or clusters of showy flowers from near the apex of the growths. These blossoms are spreading, and have the lateral sepals joined to form a more or less prominent spurlike chin. The lip is often highly colored and larger than the other floral segments. Many of the species bear notably fragrant flowers, and an impressive number of fabulous hybrids is on record.

CULTURE: In a genus as large as *Dendrobium*, it is difficult to establish one inflexible set of cultural requirements. In those species which are native to the Indo-Burmese area (such as the *D. nobile* group), the plants should be grown in baskets or pots tightly packed with osmunda, subjected to considerable heat and high humidity while actively growing, with a cooler situation and definite rest-period obligatory when the growths are mature. The tropical species, from Indonesia, Australia, and similar areas (such as *D. bigibbum* var. *Phalaenopsis*, *D. anosmum*, and others) require about the same general cultural conditions, with more heat and direct sunlight, and only partially reduced moisture—with no rest-period—upon maturation of the growths. Dendrobiums do not take kindly to overpotting, and whether grown in pots or baskets, should be given copious amounts of broken crock to assure perfect drainage. They will not tolerate for very long a soggy or stale compost. Most of the species and hybrids flower in a relatively short time from seed. All Dendrobiums benefit materially by frequent and liberal applications of fertilizing solution. (C,I,H)

D. aggregatum (ag-re-*gah*-tum)   (China; Himalayas to Burma)

Dwarf species, with clustered, rather wrinkled, yellowish pbs. to 3" tall. Lf. solitary, rigidly fleshy, dark green, about 5" long. Infls. pendulous or arching, with 12 or more fls. to 2" across. Fls. fragrant of honey,

REG S. DAVIS   JACK BRANT, JR.

Dendrobium anosmum   *Dendrobium chrysotoxum*

THE PRINCIPAL CULTIVATED ORCHIDS   147

long-lived, vivid yellow, sometimes almost orange-yellow, flattened, the lip darker orange-yellow, rounded, fuzzy. Spring. (I)

D. anosmum (an-*os*-mum) (Philippines; Malaysia; Indonesia)

Usually grown under the synonymous name of *D. superbum*. Pbs. stemlike, mostly pendulous, to 6' long. Lvs. rather small, leathery, soon deciduous. Fls. solitary or paired from the bare nodes, to 4" across, very heavily fragrant. Ss. and ps. rose-purple (very rarely pure white), with rather prominent darker veins. Lip tubular at base, dark rich rose-magenta, fuzzy and paler toward base. Late winter–spring. (I,H)

D. bigibbum var. **Phalaenopsis** (bye-*gib*-um fal-eye-*nop*-siss)
(Australia; New Guinea)

True species rarely cultivated, the variety usually seen under the synonymous name of *Dendrobium Phalaenopsis*. Pbs. erect, to 5' tall, rather slender, with a few stiffly leathery, evergreen lvs. toward the apex. Infls. usually several per growth, terminal, to 4' long, erect or arching, with 25 or more fls. each. Fls. 2½–4" across, variable in color, typically dark rose shaded with magenta, the lip much darker, flattened. Mostly winter–spring. (I,H)

D. nobile (*noe*-bi-lee) (China to Burma)

Very popular and extremely variable. Pbs. erect or arching, rather stout, the nodes irregularly swollen, mostly yellowish green, to 3' tall. Lvs. leathery, deciduous, dark glossy green, about 5" long. Fls. solitary, paired, or in 3's from the naked nodes, to 3½" across, fragrant, long-lasting. Ss. and ps. typically white, tipped with rich rose-magenta. Lip mostly white, with a dark, often almost black-magenta blotch in the curved throat, and often a lighter magenta frontal margin. Winter–spring. (C,I)

DENDROCHILUM
(den-droe-*kye*-lum)

Dendrochilum is a genus of about 150 species of epiphytic or litho-phytic orchids in the Asiatic and Indonesian tropics, related to *Coelogyne*, and usually incorrectly known as *Platyclinis*. Most of the relatively few cultivated members of the group have prominent, rather narrow, egg-shaped or cylindrical pseudobulbs, topped by a solitary leathery or papery leaf. The generally arching or sharply pendulous, densely many-flowered racemes arise from the tops of the pseudobulbs, and often attain a considerable length. The individual blossoms are small, subtended by prominent papery bracts, are usually extremely fragrant, and occur in a wide range of colors. These handsome plants are often called "Foxtail Orchids," in allusion to the extremely dense, brushlike racemes of blooms.

CULTURE: As for the species of *Coelogyne*, in accordance with the place of origin of the plant under consideration. (I,H)

Dendrobium Pierardii   *Dendrobium x Sunda Island*

D. filiforme (fi-li-*for*-mee)   (Philippines)

Pbs. about 1½" tall, clustered, the rather narrow apical lf. to 8" long, erect. Infls. racemose, on very long, thin stalks which extend outward in a graceful curve, then hang down sharply to a total length of as much as 2'. Fls. extremely numerous, less than ½" across, fragrant, yellowish-white, the lip yellow. Summer. (I,H)

D. glumaceum (gloo-*mah*-see-um)   (Philippines)

Pbs. clustered, to 3" tall, the solitary lf. to almost 1' long and about 4–5" broad. Infls. racemose, to 1' long, gracefully arching, densely many-fld., the floral bracts tan, prominent. Fls. almost 1" across, fragrant (the odor reminiscent of sweet hay), cream-white, the lip generally greenish yellow. Mostly spring. (I,H)

Dendrochilum glumaceum

Gardeners' Chronicle

DIACRIUM
(die-*ak*-ree-um)

This genus contains about four somewhat variable species of epiphytes and lithophytes in the West Indies and Central America, only one of which, *Diacrium bicornutum*, commonly known as the "Virgin Orchid," is at all frequent in cultivation. These fine orchids have thick pseudobulbs, usually hollow and inhabited by fire-ants in their native haunts, leathery yellow-green foliage, and erect spikes of showy waxen white or cream-white flowers. The blossoms are often strongly fragrant. *Diacrium* is now correctly known as *Caularthron*, but this name is not as yet accepted by horticulturists.

CULTURE: These plants demand the cultural conditions recommended for the hot-growing pseudobulbous Epidendrums and Cattleyas. They thrive in almost full sun, and should be grown rather on the dry side. (I,H)

D. bicornutum (bye-kor-*noo*-tum)   (Trinidad, Guianas, Venezuela)

Pbs. stout, hollow, mostly yellow-green, to 1' tall, but usually shorter. Lvs. few, leathery, to 8" long and 2" broad. Infls. erect, to 20" tall, with up to 15 large and spectacular blossoms. Fls. 2–3" across, fragrant, waxy, lasting well, pure glittering white, the lip also white, but usually sparsely purple-spotted, with a fleshy yellow crest in the middle. Summer. (I,H)

DISA
(*dee*-zah)

Disas, of which approximately 200 species are known, were formerly very popular in English and Continental collections, their often extremely showy flowers being widely appreciated. Gradually they are returning to fashion, and it may be expected that soon they will find the place they deserve in most orchidists' collections. These are primarily terrestrial plants, native to Africa, Malagasy (Madagascar) and the Mascarene Islands; there is also a rather large series of artificially produced hybrids. The flowers of *Disa*, in which the dorsal sepal is usually greatly enlarged (much in the manner of a lip), occur in almost every shade of the rainbow, though red, green, and blue are perhaps the most frequent hues. The petals and lip, often along with the lateral sepals, are frequently somewhat reduced in size, when compared with the dorsal sepal.

CULTURE: Because the members of this relatively large genus occur under a wide variety of natural conditions, and range from near sealevel in hot areas to high in the cool mountains, certain fluctuations naturally exist in their suggested cultural recommendations. The majority of the cultivated members of *Disa* are found at moderately high elevations, and hence demand cool or at least intermediate temperatures. They do best in relatively shallow, perfectly-drained pots (or fern pans), in a compost made up of about equal parts of shredded osmunda, fibrous loam, gritty white sand, and chopped sphagnum moss. A top-dressing of fresh, green sphagnum moss is strongly suggested. Constant moisture at the roots seems obligatory while these splendid plants are growing, but the subterranean tubers need a brief rest-period after the flowering-stems die down. Applications of somewhat weakened fertilizing solution at frequent intervals seem highly beneficial to all of the cultivated species. (C,I)

D. cornuta (kor-*noo*-tah)   (South Africa)

Sts. leafy, to about 1½′ tall. Lvs. few, to 6″ long, spotted underneath with dull red. Fls. numerous in a dense raceme, about 1½″ across. Dorsal sepal greenish marked with purple-brown at base. Lateral sepals greenish. Lip whitish marked with purple. Summer. (I)

D. uniflora (oo-ni-*floe*-rah)   (Cape of Good Hope)

One of the most beautiful and famous of all terrestrial orchids, usually grown under the synonymous name of *D. grandiflora*. Pls. to 2' tall or more. Lvs. few, rather leathery, to about 9" long. Fls. 1–5 in number, to almost 4" in diameter. Dorsal sepal erect, scarlet or orange-red, becoming whitish streaked with dark red below. Lateral sepals scarlet. Ps. and lip small, whitish to reddish. Summer–early fall. (C)

Disa x kewensis

The Orchid Journal

EPIDENDRUM
(ep-i-*den*-drum)

One of the larger orchid genera, *Epidendrum* contains well over one thousand species distributed from North Carolina to Argentina. The plants are amazingly variable in form, and are either terrestrial, lithophytic, or epiphytic in habit. One section of the genus (*Euepidendrum*) consists of elongate-stemmed plants bearing alternate, usually fleshy leaves and a terminal cluster or raceme of more or less showy flowers of variable hue. Another group (*Encyclium*) is composed of mostly epiphytic or lithophytic species with short-conical, egg-shaped, or cylindrical pseudobulbs bearing one or a few leathery leaves at the apex and a raceme of showy spreading blossoms, of every color combination imaginable. Many Epidendrums are in cultivation today, and there is a large series of truly spectacular hybrid forms. The genus is often split into a series of confusing segregate groups.

CULTURE: The cultural requirements of *Epidendrum* are basically those suggested for *Cattleya*, though the long-stemmed ("reed-stem") types are often grown much in the manner recommended for the climbing kinds of *Arachnis*, or for *Arundina*. Most of them do very well if grown non-stop, without an appreciable rest-period of any sort whatsoever. Temperature requirements fluctuate tremendously, since the component members of the genus range from hot sea-level areas to upwards of 13,000 feet in the cold Andes of South America. (C,I,H)

E. atropurpureum (at-row-pur-*pur*-ee-um)   (Tropical America)

Variable and handsome. Pbs. egg-shaped, glossy, to 4″ tall, mostly suffused with dark red-purple. Lvs. 2 or 3, leathery, heavy, to 18″ long. Infls. racemose, erect or arching, with 4–20 spectacular, fragrant, heavy-textured fls. up to 3″ across. Ss. and ps. chocolate-brown, margined with pale apple-green. Lip very large and spreading, in the typical phase pure white with a bright magenta, veined, median blotch. The forma *roseum*, found over most of the range of the typical species, differs in its more or less vivid rose-magenta lip, marked with darker magenta, and often dark chocolate ss. and ps. Mostly spring–early summer. (I,H)

Epidendrum atropurpureum

PAINTING BY G. C. K.
DUNSTERVILLE

E. cochleatum (koh-lee-*ah*-tum)   (South Florida to Brazil)

Widespread, variable. Pbs. rather flattened, mostly pear-shaped, clustered, to 6″ tall. Lvs. paired or in 3's, usually light green, to 8″ long and 1½″ broad. Infls. erect or arching, to 2′ tall, with a dozen or more fls. which open gradually and which remain fresh for many weeks. Fls. to 3″ long, not as wide, inverted, often faintly sweet-scented. Ss. and ps. narrow, rather twisted, mostly pale yellow or yellowish green. Lip round, usually dark velvety red-purple-black, marked sparsely toward the middle with light yellowish purple, shaped like a shell. Almost everblooming. (I,H)

E. ibaguense (ib-ah-*gwen*-see)   (Central and South America)

Usually known by its synonym, *E. radicans*. Sts. elongated, branching, to 7′ long, often forming a large dense tangle many feet in extent,

Epidendrum difforme

with numerous white aerial roots and alternate rigidly fleshy lvs. to 5″ long and 1″ wide. Infls. terminal, erect or arching under the weight of the fls., to 4′ tall, often producing accessory racs. for more than one season. Fls. numerous or few, in dense or loose headlike clusters as much as 6″ across, about ¾″ in diameter, the typical phase with vivid orange-red ss. and ps., the large lip with deeply toothed lobes, often bright yellow with sparse crimson spots in the middle. Summer, though often everblooming. (I,H)

ERIA
(*ee*-ree-ah)

Although more than 550 species of *Eria* have been described, these are virtually unknown to the average present-day hobbyist. The group is closely related to *Dendrobium*, and many of its members are remarkably handsome and showy orchids which should be far better known by collectors who appreciate the smaller-flowered components of this great family. Primarily epiphytic or lithophytic, Erias are extremely diverse plants both vegetatively and florally. Over their range—which extends from China and the Himalayas throughout Southeast Asia, the Philippines, and Indonesia to New Guinea—the plants occur from near sea-level to very high in the snowy mountains.

CULTURE: As for *Dendrobium*, depending upon the particular species or individual under consideration. (C,I,H)

E. rhodoptera (row-*dop*-te-rah)   (Philippines)

Pbs. usually cylindrical, mostly covered by persistent lf.-sheaths, to 5″ tall. Lvs. 2 or 3 at pb.-apex, leathery, glossy, to 7″ long. Infls. produced from upper pb.-nodes, erect or arching, rather densely many-fld., to 6″ long, furnished with large, blunt, yellowish or whitish bracts. Fls. about ½″ long, not opening widely, the ss. and ps. yellowish white, the complex lip with magenta-red lat. lbs. Mostly spring. (I,H)

E. spicata (spi-*kah*-tah)   (Himalayas to Burma)

Usually grown under its synonym, *E. convallarioides*. Pbs. oblong or thickly spindle-shaped, mostly covered by persistent lf.-sheaths, to 8″ tall, sometimes to 1″ in diam. Lvs. 3 or 4, mostly apical, thickly leathery, to 7″ long. Infls. about 4–6″ tall, the stalk about half that length, usually nodding, very densely many-fld., elongate-egg-shaped, with prominent membranous bracts. Fls. fragrant, about ½″ across, cup-shaped, pure translucent white or straw-yellow, the lip usually golden-yellow at front, the outside of the ss. often conspicuously covered with glandular hairs. Mostly spring. (I)

Eria rhodoptera

REG S. DAVIS

ERIOPSIS

(ee-ree-*awp*-siss)

This is a genus of about a half-dozen species of epiphytic (rarely litho-phytic) orchids, somewhat allied to *Gongora* and *Acineta*, native from Costa Rica to Peru and Brazil. Although rare in cultivation, their flowers, which are typically borne in large numbers in erect racemes, are very beautiful and make them well worthy of further attention by enthusiasts. The plants consist of clustered egg- or pear-shaped pseudo-bulbs, topped by a few large, leathery leaves. The basal inflorescences frequently attain a height of several feet.

CULTURE: Mostly inhabiting high elevations, the species of *Eriopsis* require cool temperatures, moisture and high humidity at all times, and relatively subdued light exposures. General culture should be that afforded *Gongora*, though the plants should be grown in well-drained pots rather than in baskets. (C,I)

E. biloba (bye-*low*-bah)   (Colombia)

Pbs. pear-shaped, to 4″ tall. Lvs. to 1′ long, heavily leathery, folded, dark green. Infls. to 1½′ tall, the rac. with many fragrant fleshy fls.

about 1½″ across. Ss. and ps. yellow, the margins bright orange-red. Lip complex in structure, yellow with more or less numerous brown spots. Mostly spring. (C,I)

E. rutidobulbon (roo-ti-doe-*bul*-bon)   (Panama; Colombia; Peru)

Pbs. pear-shaped, almost black, covered with innumerable wrinkles, to 5″ tall. Lvs. rather thick, folded. Infls. erect or arching, to almost 2′ tall. Fls. about 2¼″ across, fragrant, rather waxy, dull orange-yellow margined with red-purple on the ss. and ps. Lip large, the lat. lbs. dull orange-red spotted with dark purple, the midlb. white spotted with dark purple. Spring–summer. (C,I)

EUANTHE
(yoo-*an*-thee)

Euanthe consists of but a single species, this a widely cultivated epiphytic orchid from the Philippines, generally known in contemporary horticulture as *Vanda Sanderiana*. Even though, vegetatively, it resembles many of the strap-leaved Vandas, the floral structure is sufficiently distinctive to warrant recognition of a different genus for this species. This spectacular plant has been utilized by breeders on a multitude of occasions, and the nomenclature of the resultant hybrids is as yet terribly confused.

CULTURE: As for the tropical Vandas. In the wild, *Euanthe* usually grows on trees close to the sea—often overhanging the waves, in fact—generally fully exposed to the tropical sun. (H)

E. Sanderiana (san-der-ee-*ah*-nah)   (Southern Philippines)

St. mostly solitary, rooting freely, leafy throughout. Lvs. numerous, rather close together, tongue-shaped, to more than 15″ long, to about 1″ broad. Infls. stout, erect or ascending, to about 1′ long, usually with 4–10 large fls. well-spaced or somewhat crowded. Fls. highly variable in dimensions and color, fragrant, very long-lived, usually 3½–4½″ in diam., often longer than wide, flattened or with the ss. and ps. somewhat reflexed marginally, the dors. sep. delicate rose-color suffused with white, the lats. somewhat larger than the dors., tawny yellow with brownish red, net-branching, prominent veins. Ps. smaller than the ss., colored like the dors. sep., with a tawny yellow blotch spotted with dull red on the side next to the lat. ss. Lip small in proportion to the other segms., 2-parted, fleshy, the deeply concave basal part usually dull tawny yellow streaked with red inside, the apical parts reddish brown somewhat suffused with tawny yellow. Col. very short, buff-yellow. Fall, mostly Sept.–Nov. (H)

Euanthe Sanderiana

WM. KIRCH—ORCHIDS, LTD.

EULOPHIA
(yoo-*low*-fee-ah)

This is an interesting genus of more than 200 species of terrestrial, epiphytic, and lithophytic orchids distributed throughout the tropical and subtropical regions of the globe, with the greatest concentration of the members in Africa. Eulophias are not widely cultivated, but most of them are well deserving of more general notice because of their easily met cultural requirements and exceedingly showy flowers. The plants are variable in appearance, though many of them, with their roughened pseudobulbs and folded leaves, resemble *Phaius*. The blossoms are produced in erect racemes or panicles, often in great numbers, and are highly diverse in appearance. The sepals and petals are either similar, or in the section *Lissochilus* (formerly considered to be a separate genus) the petals are markedly larger than the other segments, more or less twisted, and often of a completely distinct hue.

The lip usually bears a small spur, and may be differently colored than the other floral parts.

CULTURE: Approximately that of the tropical species of *Phaius*. (I,H)

E. alta (*al*-tah)   (S. Florida to Brazil; W. Africa)

A handsome, variable orchid, to 6′ tall, generally somewhat shorter. Pbs. cormlike, in a long creeping series, usually subterranean, to 3″ across, flattened, giving rise to a tuft of folded dark green lvs. to 4′ tall

Eulophia alta

DRAWING BY BLANCHE AMES

and mostly less than 6″ wide. Infls. rather woody, erect, to 6′ tall, bearing a raceme of handsome, variable, long-lived fls. at the apex. Fls. fragrant, about 1½″ across, typically with green-purple or maroon upstanding ss. and ps., and an intricate, somewhat cup-shaped, dark maroon-purple lip. Mostly late fall. (I)

E. guineensis (gi-nee-*en*-sis)   (W. Tropical Africa)

Pbs. clustered, to 2″ tall, roughly furrowed, irregular in shape. Lvs. usually paired, folded, deciduous, to 2′ long, about 6″ broad. Infls. raceme-like, mostly erect, to 3′ tall, bearing a dozen or more large and handsome blooms. Fls. almost 3″ across, fragrant, long-lasting. Ss. and ps. dull green-purple, the lat. ss. resting on the sides of the lip when the fls. are completely opened. Lip very large, mostly pure white, with the large median lobe flushed and marked with dark rose-red in the center. Summer. (H)

EULOPHIELLA
(yoo-low-fee-*el*-ah)

Four species of the genus *Eulophiella* are known, all of them found on the island of Malagasy (Madagascar) and nowhere else in the world. Formerly considered to be placed in the *Cymbidium* alliance, the group is now generally referred to the subtribe *Cyrtopodiinae*. Singularly handsome epiphytic orchids, Eulophiellas are exceedingly rare in collections these days, though they formerly were rather frequently grown in England and on the Continent by connoisseurs. Consisting of elongate pseudobulbs and long leathery foliage, the plants give rise to erect or arching racemes of large and beautiful flowers of brilliant hue and long-lasting qualities. A fine hybrid, *Eulophiella x Rolfei* (*E. Elisabethae* × *E. Roempleriana*) has been registered, and is still occasionally seen in choice collections.

CULTURE: Eulophiellas have long had the reputation of being difficult orchids to grow and flower successfully, but if a few rules are followed their cultural requirements may be met with ease. Since they are native to tropical, humid Madagascar, a warm moist situation is required, and the plants must never be permitted to become dry, though the drainage of the compost must be such that souring never occurs. A suitable compost is as follows: 1 part chopped osmunda (or tree-fern fiber), 1 part chopped fresh sphagnum moss, and 1 part chopped leaf-mould, all of these ingredients thoroughly mixed together. Because of the rampantly elongating rhizomes, large slatted baskets, rather than pots, are usually used for these orchids. They dislike being disturbed, hence should be divided only when necessary. Strong sunlight and sharp drafts of chill air must be avoided at all times, although an excess of shade is also frowned upon. (H)

E. Elisabethae (ee-*liz*-ah-beth-eye)   (Madagascar)

Robust epiphyte, to more than 4′ tall when in flower. Habit as in the genus. Infl. to about 2′ long, usually almost horizontal, bearing 12–15 showy fls. in a rather dense apical raceme. Fls. fragrant, waxy, to about 2″ across, opening widely. Ss. and ps. glittering white flushed with delicate rose. Lip white with a large bright yellow median blotch. Spring. (H)

Eulophiella x Rolfei   *Gastrochilus bellinus*

GASTROCHILUS
(gass-*traw*-ki-luss)

Gastrochilus is a genus of about 15 species of epiphytic (very rarely lithophytic) orchids native in the region extending from Japan and the Himalayas to Indonesia. A few of them are on occasion found in particularly choice contemporary collections, where they are almost invariably listed under the incorrect generic name of *Saccolabium*, which applies to a completely distinct group of the alliance. Both vegetatively and florally, the species of *Gastrochilus* are highly diverse plants, which should be far better appreciated by hobbyists.

CULTURE: As for *Vanda*, depending upon the species or individual and its place of origin. (I,H)

G. bellinus (*bel*-i-nuss)   (Burma)

Usually known by its synonym of *Saccolabium bellinum*. St. very stout and short, usually less than 2″ tall. Lvs. mostly 6–8, narrowly tongue-shaped, rigidly leathery, to 8″ long and 1¼″ broad. Infls. usually erect, densely 4–7-fld., the scape robust. Fls. fragrant, waxy, long-lasting, about 1½″ across, the ss. and ps. greenish yellow with purple spots and blotches, the complex lip white spotted with dull or vivid red, the middle part with a tuft of hairs on each side, the center bright yellow. Late winter–spring. (I)

G. calceolaris (kal-see-oh-*lah*-riss)   (Himalayas to Indonesia)

Usually known by the synonym *Saccolabium calceolare*. St. stout, very short. Lvs. 3–6, tongue-shaped, leathery, to 7″ long and ¾″ broad. Infls. very short, few-fld., the stout scape purple-spotted. Fls. about ¾″ in diam., waxy, somewhat fragrant, lasting rather well, the ss. and ps. greenish or yellowish with brown or purplish spots, the sac of the very complex lip yellow outside, with brown spots, the small lat. lbs. white, the midlb. with fringed white margins and a fleshy orange central part, the col. purplish. Fall. (I,H)

GOMESA
(go-*mee*-zah)

Gomesa is a genus allied to *Oncidium* and containing about 10 species of dwarf, singularly attractive epiphytic orchids, all of which are endemic to Brazil. They are seldom encountered in contemporary collections, though their free-flowering habit and ease of cultivation recommend them to all hobbyists. Pseudobulbous plants, they produce arching, densely many-flowered racemes of oddly shaped, fragrant, greenish, yellowish, or whitish blossoms with great lasting qualities.

Culture: The Gomesas require the same conditions as do the tropical Oncidiums with pseudobulbs. (I,H)

G. crispa (*kriss*-pah)   (Brazil)

Pbs. egg-shaped, somewhat flattened, usually yellowish, about 4″ tall. Lvs. paired, leathery, to 8″ long. Infls. racemose, pendulous or arching, densely many-fld., to 8″ long. Fls. about ¾″ long, fragrant, yellow-green, with all of the segments very crisped and wavy-margined, the lat. ss. joined at the base, their tips spreading. Spring–summer. (I,H)

GONGORA
(*gon*-goe-rah)

Gongora contains about 30 species of epiphytic and lithophytic orchids, distributed from Mexico to Brazil, characterized by pendulous or arching racemes of fantastically contorted flowers which often exhale a heavy sweet odor. The plants resemble *Stanhopea* in habit, having furrowed and wrinkled pseudobulbs and plicate foliage. The flowers are mostly medium-sized, generally in shades of brown, purplish, red or yellow, and are frequently very numerous, in long, graceful, tightly packed racemes. Gongoras are at present seldom cultivated, though their intriguing formation makes them among the most interesting of

Gomesa Glaziovii

Flora Brasílica

the "botanical" genera of orchids. The genus *Acropera* is referable here. A common name for *Gongora* is "Punch-and-Judy Orchids," given because of the supposed resemblance of the flowers to hand-puppets.

Culture: These fine orchids should be grown in baskets or on slabs of tree-fern, because of the generally outward-arching and pendulous nature of the inflorescences. Their general cultural requirements otherwise are those of *Stanhopea*. (I,H)

G. armeniaca (ar-men-ee-*ah*-kah)   (Central America)

Usually grown as *Acropera armeniaca*. Pbs. rather conical, about 3″ tall at most, deeply furrowed. Lvs. several, stalked, to 2′ long, mostly erect, folded. Racs. sharply drooping, to 3′ long, bearing up to 30 handsome, fragrant blossoms. Fls. about 2″ across, with slender reflexed ss. and ps. that are generally orange-yellow, irregularly barred with red-brown. Lip almost saclike, very fleshy, brownish yellow, sometimes dotted with purple. Summer. (I)

G. galeata (gal-ee-*ah*-tah)   (Mexico)

Often grown as *Acropera Loddigesii*. Similar to *G. armeniaca* in habit, but somewhat smaller in all parts. Fls. about 12 in number, to

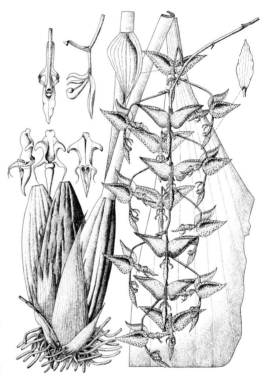

Gongora nigrita

Flora Brasílica

1½″ across, very fragrant and rather short-lived. Ss. and ps. Nankeen-yellow, suffused with brownish, broader than those of most of the species, sharply reflexed, the dors. sep. curved over the rest of the flower like a hood. Lip dark brown-yellow. Mostly summer. (I)

GRAMMATOPHYLLUM
(gram-at-oh-*fil*-um)

This genus is made up of about 8 epiphytic or terrestrial species from the Asiatic-Indonesian-Melanesian region, some of which are of enormous size. The plants are of two basic types—either with tremendously elongate, canelike pseudobulbs, or with short *Cymbidium*-like ones. The flowers, produced in prodigious numbers, are mostly fleshy in texture, and are typically colored yellow or green with brown, red or purple markings. Here belongs the largest orchid known, *Grammatophyllum speciosum*, the "Queen Orchid," which has arching or pendulous pseudobulbs attaining an ultimate length of more than 25 feet. Still uncommon in cultivation, Grammatophyllums are decidedly worthy of more extensive interest.

CULTURE: Grammatophyllums of the *G. speciosum* group, because of their gigantic stature, should be cultivated in special beds, with a compost similar to that afforded *Arachnis*. The smaller species, such as *G. Measuresianum* and *G. scriptum*, prefer basket-culture, under conditions similar to those given the tropical species of *Dendrobium*. Abundant water and heat at all times are essential to their success. (H)

G. Measuresianum (may-zur-zee-*ah*-num) (Philippines)

Pbs. clustered, very robust, to 10″ tall and 5″ wide. Lvs. leathery, dark glossy green, to 3′ long. Infls. stiffly erect or arching under the weight of the fls., to 7′ tall, with up to 70 handsome and fragrant fls. Fls. about 4″ across, waxy, long-lasting. Ss. and ps. chartreuse spotted and blotched with brown-purple or reddish brown. Lip small, greenish yellow marked with purple. An exceedingly handsome and spectacular orchid. Spring–early summer. (H)

G. scriptum (*skrip*-tum) (Philippines to New Guinea)

A highly variable species, allied to **G.** *Measuresianum*, and resembling it in habit. Infls. mostly arching to pendulous, to 5′ long, with 150 or more fls., usually several infls. produced from each growth. Fls. about 2½″ across, fragrant, often not opening fully, yellow-green thickly spotted with red-brown in the typical form. Lip small, mostly dark maroon. Spring–summer. (H)

G. speciosum (spee-see-*oh*-sum) (Malaya; Indonesia to New Guinea)

The most robust of all orchids. Pbs. to more than 25′ long (though generally shorter), canelike, cylindrical, rather slender. Lvs. very numerous, to 5′ long, narrow, leathery. Infls. to 8′ tall, very stout, often with more than 100 spectacular fragrant fls. to 8″ across. Ss. and ps. fleshy, spreading, golden or brownish yellow, more or less densely blotched with red-brown or red-purple. Lip small, yellow marked with red-brown or red-purple. Summer. (H)

Grammatophyllum scriptum

REG S. DAVIS

HEXISEA
(hek-*sih*-zee-ah)

A genus of about 6 species in Mexico, Central America, and northern South America, *Hexisea* is as yet comparatively little known in our collections, although it contains one of the handsomest of the small "botanical" orchids. A member of the subtribe *Laeliinae*, it is somewhat allied to *Epidendrum*, but differs in both the peculiar vegetative habit and the structure of the flowers, which are borne in short, fewflowered apical racemes. The pseudobulbs are either branched or—more commonly—superimposed, one on top of the other, thus giving a unique appearance to the plants, even when not in bloom.

CULTURE: Hexiseas are easily grown, requiring a minimum of care at all times. In general they should be treated much like the intermediate types of *Epidendrum*, with abundant moisture and light while actively growing, and a rather strict period of rest upon completion of the new growths. A well-drained compost of straight osmunda fiber, tightly packed, suits them well, and moderate applications of fertilizer or manure-water may be given with benefit. (I,H)

H. bidentata (bye-den-*tah*-tah)   (Mexico to N. South America)

Pls. sometimes to 3′ tall, very variable in dimensions and form. Pbs. rather slender, superimposed, the sections usually about 4″ long. Lvs.

paired, at the apex of each pb.-section, thinly leathery. Fls. several, in a rather compact cluster, opening widely, to as much as 1″ in diam., varying from vermilion to scarlet, the lip often with a dull purple basal blotch, but in shape almost identical with other segms. Mostly spring. (I,H)

HOULLETIA
(hoo-*leh*-tee-ah)

Houlletia consists of about 8 species of often very handsome terrestrial, epiphytic, or lithophytic orchids, allied to *Paphinia* and rather distantly to *Gongora*, native in Central and South America. They have rather prominent pseudobulbs, topped by a solitary, large, folded leaf, and give rise to arching, erect, or pendulous racemes of usually showy blossoms. Although at one time the Houlletias were widely grown in England and Europe, they are seldom encountered today, even in the choicest collections.

CULTURE: As for *Gongora*. (I,H)

H. Brocklehurstiana (brok-ul-hurs-tee-*ah*-nah) (Brazil)

Pbs. egg-shaped, about 3″ tall. Lf. narrowed below into a stalk, to 1½′ long, rather heavy-textured. Spike erect, to 1½′ tall, with 5–10 handsome flls. about 3″ in diam., of waxy texture and with a heady fragrance. Ss. and ps. dark brown-red flecked with yellow in the lower half. Lip very complex, mostly yellow with red markings, the front lb. magenta-red. Winter. (I,H)

H. odoratissima (oh-do-rah-*ti*-si-mah) (Colombia)

Resembling *H. Brocklehurstiana* in habit. Spike erect, to almost 2′ tall. Fls. 6–10, to 3″ across, fragrant, waxy. Ss. and ps. dark lustrous chocolate-brown. Lip white, sometimes dotted with violet toward the front. Fall–early winter. (I)

HUNTLEYA
(*hunt*-lee-yah)

This is a small group of 3 or 4 species of spectacular epiphytic orchids of the American tropics, ranging from Costa Rica to Brazil. The genus is frequently reduced to synonymy under *Zygopetalum*, but most recent orchidologists have placed it in a separate subtribe, the *Huntleyinae*. The plants consist of rather thin-textured leaves, arranged to form a loose fan, from the axils of which the 1-flowered scapes are produced. The flowers of the only *Huntleya* in cultivation are large, waxy, lacquered and incredibly handsome; they last for several weeks in perfection.

CULTURE: Primarily highland epiphytes, Huntleyas are best cultivated in the coolhouse with Odontoglossums, Miltonias, and the like. A scant compost of rather loose, very well-drained osmunda is satis-

Houlletia Brocklehurstiana

Flora Brasílica

factory, with a top-dressing of sphagnum moss to assist in retention of moisture. The plants must never be permitted to become dry, since no pseudobulbous moisture-storing organs are present. Rather diffused light is required for best flower-production. Stale conditions at the roots must be avoided, or the death of the plant will quickly result. (C,I)

H. meleagris (mel-ee-*ag*-riss) (Costa Rica to Brazil)

Syn: *H. Burtii.* A rare but very desirable orchid. Lvs. forming a fan to 1′ tall in robust specimens, rather folded, generally light green. Infls. 6–12″ tall, mostly erect, usually from upper lf.-axils, 1-fld. Fls. fragrant, waxy, very shiny, to 5″ across, long-lasting. Ss. with the apical ⅔ a lustrous reddish brown, often with a few yellow spots, the basal ⅓ white or pale yellow. Ps. similar in color to the ss., but usually with some basal purple markings. Lip fleshy and complex, basally white, front half of apical lb. rich waxy red-brown or brown-purple, the crest fringed. Summer. (C,I)

Huntleya meleagris

Gardening World

IONOPSIS
(eye-oh-*nop*-siss)

Ionopsis contains 3 or 4 extremely variable, dwarf epiphytic orchids, which are widespread from South Florida through the West Indies to South America. The pseudobulbs are typically tiny and almost obscured by the proportionately large, thick or cylindrical leaves. The delicate little flowers are often borne in great numbers in an airy, branched panicle, and are usually white, lilac or pale purple, frequently with darker veins or markings.

CULTURE: The cultivation of *Ionopsis* is often a rather difficult matter, because the plants are basically fragile, being intolerant of improper conditions or neglect. The best results are obtained by growing them rather on the dry side, affixed to smallish slabs of tree-fern fiber, in a bright (but not directly sunny) situation, where fresh air is readily available. Particular attention must be paid to the condition of the fiber on which they are grown, for even the slightest bit of staleness will result in their rapid deterioration. (I)

I. utricularioides (yoo-trik-yoo-lah-ree-*oy*-deez)   (Tropical America)

A widespread and extremely variable species. Pbs. virtually absent.

Lvs. thick, tufted, to 6″ long. Infls. to 2′ tall, simple or panicled, arching or erect, many-fld. Fls. about ½″ long, varying from pure white through blush-white with lilac veins to dark lavender, with the very small ss. and ps. clustered at the base of the large lobed lip. Mostly winter–early spring. (I)

Ionopsis utricularioides

DRAWING BY BLANCHE AMES

IPSEA
(*ip*-see-ah)

This genus contains but one species, the famed "Daffodil Orchid" of Ceylon. A graceful, slender-growing terrestrial plant, it consists of a few grasslike leaves arising from a small subterranean tuber, and 2–6-flowered erect racemes of brilliant yellow blossoms of great beauty. Ipseas are seldom seen in collections today, since their treatment under artificial conditions is rather difficult and the plants do not long thrive away from their native meadows.

CULTURE: The tubers should be placed in small pots, in a perfectly drained compost of about 3 parts loam and 1 part of mixed leaf-mould and shredded green sphagnum. Broken crock and granite gravel may advantageously be mixed through this medium. A warm, constantly moist, rather sunny situation is necessary while the plants are actively growing, but after flowering, removal to a cooler, shaded spot is required, and water must be stopped almost entirely until the new shoots appear. The foliage is deciduous each year, and annual repotting is recommended. (I,H)

I. speciosa (spee-see-*oh*-sah)   (Ceylon; Southern India)

Pbs. usually underground, conical, about 1″ tall. Lvs. about 1′ long, narrow, folded, few in number. Spike to 1½′ tall, the fls. solitary or paired (rarely to 6) at the apex. Fls. fragrant, lasting well, about 3″ in diam., pale or bright golden-yellow, the lip usually somewhat darker. Winter. (I,H)

ISOCHILUS
(iss-*aw*-ki-luss)

Isochilus, as now understood, contains two variable species of unusually interesting grasslike orchids, either epiphytic or lithophytic, native in the American tropics from Mexico and Cuba to Brazil. Now placed in the subtribe *Ponerinae*, they are allied to *Ponera* and to *Jacquiniella*, and are occasionally encountered in choice collections of "botanicals." Elongate, pendulous or erect stems are thickly set with strap-shaped, rather thin leaves. At the top they bear tight or rather loose racemes of small, bright magenta (to pink or orange) blossoms which do not open fully.

CULTURE: *Isochilus linearis* is so easily grown that it is admirably suited to the amateur's collection. Kept in a warm, rather shady spot, it can be readily brought into flower. A pot, rather tightly filled with well-drained osmunda, is best as a container. This must never be allowed to dry out, though if it begins to sour, repotting should be attended to immediately. Division should be done if the inner portions of the clump begin to die, but should otherwise not be attempted. (I,H)

I. linearis (lin-ee-*ah*-riss)   (Cuba and Mexico southward)

Stems very thin, to 2′ tall, often arching or pendulous, densely leafy throughout. Lvs. rather thin and narrow, to 4″ long, usually less than ¼″ broad. Fls. several to many in a dense or loose apical rac. or head, about ½″ long, not opening widely. Ss. and ps. varying from almost pink or orange to vivid magenta, the lip sometimes marked with dark magenta. Various times throughout the year, sometimes almost ever-blooming. (I,H)

Isochilus linearis

DRAWING BY ALEX D. HAWKES

LAELIA
(*lie*-lee-ah)

Among the most popular of all orchids, the 75 or more species of this primarily epiphytic or lithophytic genus extend from Mexico to Cuba to Argentina, with the center of development in Brazil. The plants mostly resemble *Cattleya* in habit and flowers, though the petals are typically narrower than in that group, and the lip less ornate. Several of the species are dwarf plants bearing tall spikes of brilliant orange or yellow blossoms of great beauty, while others (such as those commonly grown under the horticultural name of *Schomburgkia*) attain prodigious dimensions, with inflorescences sometimes 10 feet or more in length. The various members of this group have been extensively hybridized with *Cattleya, Brassavola, Sophronitis,* and others, and a complex series of artificial aggregations is the result.

CULTURE: The cultural requirements of Laelias approximate those of *Cattleya,* though in general the Laelias seem more appreciative of full sun. (C,I,H)

L. anceps (*an*-seps) (Mexico, Honduras)

A handsome, variable and popular orchid. Pbs. usually 4-angled, to 6″ tall, with a single stiffly leathery, glossy green lf. Infls. apical, to 7′ tall, erect or gracefully arching, the stalk sharp-edged, with a cluster of 1–6 fls. at the apex. Fls. to 4½″ across, fragrant, very beautiful. Ss. and ps. usually dark rose, the lip lustrous crimson-purple, the lat. lbs. yellow or yellowish with crimson marks. Mostly winter. (C,I)

L. cinnabarina (sin-ah-bar-*ee*-nah) (Brazil)

Pbs. cylindrical, elongated, narrowed apically, to 10″ tall, usually flushed with red or red-purple. Lf. solitary, thick and rigid, erect, as long as the pb. Infl. erect, to 2′ tall, with a cluster of 5–20 fls. at apex. Fls. to 3″ across, star-shaped, brilliant orange-red, the lip usually slightly darker. Spring. (I,H)

L. purpurata (pur-pur-*ah*-tah) (Brazil)

Pbs. robust, club-shaped, often yellow-green, to about 8″ tall. Lf. solitary, thick and leathery, dark green, to 2′ long. Infls. short, with up to 12 large fls. Fls. to 9″ across, with rather slender ss., the ps. somewhat broader, all of these typically white. Lip tubular, dark rich velvety crimson-purple, the throat yellow, streaked with magenta-crimson. A very variable and handsome orchid, perhaps the most majestic in the genus. Late winter–summer. (I,H)

L. tibicinis (tib-i-*si*-niss) (Central America)

Pbs. yellow, woody, to 3′ tall, swollen-cylindrical, hollow, usually inhabited by stinging ants. Lvs. several, stiffly rigid, yellow-green, to 1′ long. Infls. erect or arching, variable in length from 5′ to as much as 15′, with a large compact rac. of handsome fls. at the tip. Fls. fragrant, variable, to 3½″ in diam., on long stalks, the segms. wavy. Ss. and ps. mostly red- or purple-brown, paler at base and on margins. Lip complex, orange-yellow, red-purple and rose-white. Usually grown under the synonymous name of *Schomburgkia.* Spring. (H)

Laelia anceps fma. *Sanderiana*

The Orchid Journal

Laelia purpurata

Laelia (Schomburgkia) undulata

LAELIOPSIS
(lye-lee-*op*-siss)

Two species of *Laeliopsis* are known to date, only one of which is at present in cultivation, and this is a rare—though very lovely—orchid. The genus is closest in its alliance to *Broughtonia*, but differs in technical characters, notably the rigidly fleshy, saw-edged leaves.

Culture: As for *Broughtonia*. (H)

L. domingensis (doe-min-*gen*-siss)   (Hispaniola)

Often grown under its synonym, *Broughtonia lilacina*. Pbs. clustered, egg-shaped to spindle-shaped, somewhat compressed, 2–3″ long. Lvs. usually 2, rigid, to 5″ long. Infls. slender, to 2′ long, with a cluster of 5–9 (or more) fls. at apex, these opening successively over a long period. Fls. to 2½″ in diam., not opening completely, often rather short-lived, at times fragrant, the ss. and ps. pale rosy mauve with purple veins and suffusions, the basally tubular lip white outside and pale yellow inside, the throat traversed by pale to dark purple lines, the flaring midlobe fringed, rose-purple with darker veins. Mostly Apr.–June. (H)

LANIUM
(*la*-nee-um)

The genus *Lanium* includes about four species of dwarf, rather elegant epiphytic or lithophytic orchids in Brazil, the Guianas, and adjacent areas. Very seldom encountered in collections today, they are delightful little plants which produce an amazing profusion of small flowers from the apices of short fat pseudobulbs. Allied to *Epidendrum*, they rather resemble certain members of that genus, but are immediately distinguishable from them on technical details.

Culture: As for the tropical, pseudobulbous species of *Epidendrum*. (H)

L. avicula (ah-*vi*-koo-lah)   (Brazil)

Pbs. borne at intervals on the creeping rhiz., about 1½″ tall. Lvs. paired, to 2″ long, rather fleshy. Infl. erect or arching, to 8″ tall, loosely many-fld. Fls. less than ½″ across, creamy or yellowish white, the lip very small. Fall. (H)

L. Berkeleyi (*burk*-lee-eye)   (Brazil)

Similar to *L. avicula*, but with longer pbs. and larger foliage. Fls.

about ¾″ across, pale green, sparsely dotted with red or magenta-red. Winter. (H)

Lanium avicula

F. C. HOEHNE

LEOCHILUS
(lee-*aw*-ki-luss)

Leochilus (sometimes misspelled *Leiochilus*) contains about a dozen species of dwarf, proportionately large-flowered epiphytic or lithophytic orchids in the American tropics from Cuba and Mexico to Argentina. Closely allied to *Oncidium*, the genus is differentiated from it by floral details. Small compressed pseudobulbs bear 1 or 2 rather large leathery leaves and give rise to basal, usually erect inflorescences of a few unusual little blossoms. The members of this interesting genus are rarely seen in our collections today, though many of them are attractive when well grown and in full flower.

CULTURE: Most members of *Leochilus* are lowland epiphytes, hence require conditions much like those afforded the warm-growing species of *Oncidum* and the pseudobulbous tropical Epidendrums. (I,H)

L. labiatus (la-bee-*ah*-tus)   (West Indies; Panama; Trinidad)

Pbs. clustered, compressed, rather glossy, about ½" tall. Lf. solitary, leathery, often reddish brown, to 3" long and ¾" wide. Infls. slender, erect or arching, few-fld., to as much as 8" long. Fls. faintly foul-smelling, about ½" across. Ss. and ps. yellow, spotted or striped with red-brown. Lip proportionately large, yellow with a red or red-brown basal blotch. Mostly spring. (I,H)

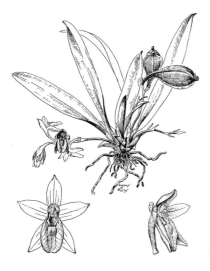

Leochilus Johnstonii

DRAWING BY GORDON W. DILLON

LEPTOTES
(lep-*toe*-teez)

Leptotes contains some 3 or 4 species of delightful and spectacular dwarf epiphytic or lithophytic orchids of the subtribe *Laeliinae*, native to Brazil and Paraguay. Although among the showiest of the "botanical" orchids when well grown, they are infrequently encountered in present-day collections. The charming Brazilian *Leptotes bicolor* is interesting in that an extract from the ripe seed-capsules is used for flavoring in the same manner as commercial vanilla. The plants consist of slender, scarcely thickened stems, topped by a fleshy, almost cylindrical leaf, from the base of which arise the short, few-flowered racemes of pro-portionately large and showy blossoms.

CULTURE: The species of *Leptotes* do best if grown in well-drained pots, filled with tightly packed osmunda fiber. Repotting often sets the plants back for several seasons, so it should be avoided whenever possible. Instead, stale compost can be carefully removed from around the roots, and fresh pieces inserted. Copious supplies of moisture and warmth are required when the plants are actively growing, but upon maturation of the new shoots, water should be somewhat withheld until root action again starts. A rather bright and sunny situation suits them best. (I,H)

L. bicolor (*bye*-ko-lor)   (Brazil; Paraguay)

St.-like pbs. usually less than 2″ tall, bearing a solitary cylindrical lf. to 6″ long, often almost pendulous. Infls. short, with 2–5 showy, extremely fragrant, long-lasting fls. to 2½″ across. Ss. and ps. rather narrow, spreading, often somewhat twisted, pure white. Lip with the sides often folded down, brilliant magenta, the margins sometimes whitish or cream-white. Mostly winter–spring. (I,H)

LOCKHARTIA
(lok-*har*-tee-ah)

This genus contains about 30 species of oddly handsome epiphytic orchids, native in the American tropics from Mexico to Peru and Brazil. Commonly known as the "Braided Orchids," because of the unique arrangement of the leaves along the stems, they are rather frequently grown today, and are easily brought into flower even by the amateur hobbyist. The rather complex, typically small flowers are usually yellow, occasionally marked with red or brown, and somewhat resemble an *Oncidium* in structure, a genus to which *Lockhartia* is vaguely related.

CULTURE: Lockhartias are found on trees at elevations ranging from near sea-level to high in the tropical mountains of the Americas. Under cultivation, they grow best in smallish, perfectly-drained pots, tightly packed with osmunda. A thin layer of fresh sphagnum moss is often added to newly acquired, unrooted specimens, to facilitate growth. Diffuse light is required. The osmunda must never be allowed to dry out, although sogginess must be equally avoided. (I,H)

L. acuta (ah-*kyu*-tah)   (Panama to Trinidad)

Usually grown under the synonymous name, *L. pallida*. Sts. flattened, generally more or less pendulous, to 2½′ long, completely covered by innumerable bright green, flat, rather triangular lvs. with incurved tips, about 1″ long or more. Fls. less than ½″ across, rather numerous over a long period of time in panicles to 3½″ long from the upper parts of the sts. Ss. and ps. usually white or cream-white, the complexly lobed, larger lip mostly butter-yellow. Almost everblooming, but with the greatest flush of fls. in spring. (I,H)

L. Oerstedii (oar-*sted*-ee-eye) (Mexico to Panama)

Among the larger-flowered members of the genus, almost identical in habit with *L. acuta*, though the plant is often smaller and the foliage sharper-pointed. Fls. to about ¾″ long, in a few-fld. rac. about ½″ long. Ss. and ps. vivid yellow, the lateral ss. sometimes red-spotted. Lip very large, complex, yellow marked with red or red-brown at the base. Spring–summer, often over a period of several months. (I,H)

LUISIA
(loo-*iss*-ee-ah)

Luisia is a genus of about 35 species of epiphytic or rarely lithophytic orchids in the Asiatic and Indonesian tropics, many of which are odd in appearance and as yet extremely uncommon in our collections. Allied to *Vanda* and other members of the subtribe *Sarcanthinae*, the plants characteristically have erect, free-rooting stems furnished with rather distant, terete leaves—much resembling *Vanda teres* and *Vanda x Miss Joaquim* in this respect—and producing usually short, few- to many-flowered racemes of intricate blossoms. Most Luisias bear flowers in shades of green, yellow or brown, often with a powerful and foetid odor. The relatively small sepals and petals surround a proportionately large and complex lip, which sometimes resembles an insect, hence the common name of "Bee Orchid" which has been applied to them.

CULTURE: Luisias are easily grown when given the conditions suggested for the tropical species of *Vanda*. (I,H)

L. teretifolia (ter-ee-ti-*foe*-lee-ah) (China to New Caledonia)

Variable in all parts, the habit as for the genus, often profusely branched near base. Infls. mostly less than 1½″ long, few-fld., closely appressed against the st. Fls. about ¾″ across, faintly foul-smelling, long-lasting, rather heavy-textured. Ss. and longer, narrower ps. yellowish or greenish yellow, the complex lip usually dull purple-brown or chocolate-brown, fuzzy, sometimes with a basal irregular yellowish blotch. Mostly fall. (I,H)

LYCASTE
(lie-*kass*-tee)

Approximately 35 species of epiphytic, lithophytic or rarely terrestrial orchids, found in the American tropics from Mexico and Cuba to Peru

Luisia Jonesii

and Brazil, make up the genus *Lycaste*. These fascinating plants bear large, showy, waxen blossoms on erect stalks from the pseudobulb-bases—the flowers always solitary, but typically produced in large numbers from the new growth. The colors vary from apple-green to pale blush-pink and pure glittering white, and the blooms frequently exhale a delicious perfume. *Lycaste virginalis* forma *alba*, a pure white phase of this popular species, is the national flower of Guatemala, and is among the most prized members of the group in collections. A considerable series of artificially produced hybrids is known, both within the genus and with allies, such as *Anguloa* and *Zygopetalum*.

CULTURE: The culture of Lycastes is generally simple. The plants do best in pots or baskets rather tightly filled with osmunda or chopped tree-fern fiber, with copious broken crock to assure perfect drainage. They delight in a moist sunny situation while in active growth, but should be afforded a rather strict rest-period—with only enough moisture supplied to prevent excessive shrivelling—when the new pseudobulbs have matured. Species which inhabit high elevations, notably *L. virginalis*, should be kept rather cool. (C,I)

L. aromatica (ah-row-*mah*-ti-kah)   (Mexico; Guatemala)

Pbs. about 2″ tall, somewhat laterally compressed, rather yellowish in color. Lvs. several, folded, to 8″ long and 2½″ broad, deciduous.

Spikes to 4″ tall, usually very numerous from the base of the matured new pbs. Fls. very waxy, heavily fragrant, lasting well, about 2½″ across or more. Ss. golden-yellow, spreading. Ps. and lip darker orange-yellow, usually spotted (especially on the lip) with orange. Winter. (C,I)

L. brevispatha (brev-i-*spah*-thah)   (Central America)

Similar in habit to *L. aromatica*, but usually somewhat larger in all parts. Fls. about 2½″–3″ across, numerous, fragrant of fresh apples. Ss. pale apple-green, blotched sparsely with light rose. Ps. white, suffused with pale rose. Lip white, with a few scattered light red-magenta spots. Spring–summer. (I)

L. virginalis (vir-ji-*nah*-liss)   (Guatemala)

Basically similar to the other species in habit, but usually much more robust. Pbs. to 8″ tall, often rather angular. Fls. to 6″ across, very waxy and fragrant, highly variable in coloration, long-lived. Ss. usually white, more or less flushed with rose. Ps. smaller, white spotted with vivid rose-red. Lip small, white spotted with rose-red and dark crimson-red. Mostly winter. (C)

Lycaste virginalis

VEITCH

MASDEVALLIA
(maz-dee-*vah*-lee-ah)

Masdevallia is generally considered to contain almost 300 species, and to produce some of the most extraordinary flowers to be found anywhere in the orchid family. Mostly epiphytes, these species range from Mexico to Bolivia and Brazil, with the majority in the high-elevation "cloud forests" of the Colombian Andes. These wondrous plants were formerly so popular with collectors that prices in excess of several thousand dollars were on occasion paid for particularly choice specimens. Gradually they are coming into fashion again but are as yet uncommon in cultivation. Masdevallias are usually small plants, but their flowers range from an inch or so across to more than a foot from tip to tip. Their relatively characteristic structure makes them easily recognizable, the sepals being broader than the petals and often furnished with long tails. In coloration they cover almost the entire gamut of the hues of the rainbow, with even an approach to black being known in certain rare forms. In addition to the numerous species, some remarkable and spectacular hybrids are known.

CULTURE: Masdevallias differ somewhat in their cultural requirements from many other orchids. Most of those found in our collections come from high altitudes, hence need the cool, highly humid and moist conditions such as are suggested for the alpine Odontoglossums. Since they have no appreciable water-storing structures, they must never be allowed to become dry, hence a perfect-draining compost is essential. Out of a number of composts that have been tried for these plants through the years, the currently approved one is made up of about equal proportions of chopped sphagnum moss and chopped or shredded osmunda fiber, preferably with a top-dressing of fresh sphagnum moss for better moisture retention. A bright but not sunny spot, with abundant fresh, freely moving air, does well for them. Species which produce pendulous flower-spikes should be kept in small baskets rather than in the pots used for the other kinds. Masdevallias are particularly susceptible to the attacks of thrips and red spider, and steps should be taken to prevent the appearance of these insects in the collection. (C,I)

M. coccinea (kok-*sin*-ee-ah)   (Colombia)

Often grown as *M. Harryana*, a synonym. Lvs. clustered, dark glossy-green, narrowed into stalks below, 6–9" long. Infls. erect, to more than 1' tall, 1-fld. Fls. heavy-textured, waxy, extremely variable in color and somewhat so in size, to about 3" long at most, the ss. ranging from white or pale yellow through orange, scarlet, crimson or magenta-red to dark rich crimson-purple. Ps., lip and col. inclosed in the sepal-tube. Mar.–June. (C)

M. tovarensis (toe-vah-*ren*-siss)   (Venezuela)

Lvs. clustered, leathery, glossy-green, 5–6″ long. Infls. to 7″ tall, 2–5-fld., 3-angled. Fls. opening widely, waxy, very long-lived, 1″ across, about 3″ long, pure white, the lat. ss. short-tailed. Ps., lip and col. small, inclosed in sepal-tube. Nov.–Feb. (C)

PAINTING BY G. C. K. DUNSTERVILLE   DRAWING BY BLANCHE AMES

Masdevallia tovarensis   *Maxillaria Camaridii*

MAXILLARIA
(max-il-*ah*-ree-ah)

Maxillaria is a genus of more than 300 species of epiphytic, lithophytic, or rarely terrestrial orchids which range from South Florida and Mexico to Argentina, with centers of development occurring in the Andes and in Brazil. The members of this unusual genus are becoming increasingly popular with hobbyists today, yet but a small percentage of them is as yet known in cultivation. The genus is a tremendously varied one, especially as regards the vegetative appearance of the plants, while the often numerous flowers fluctuate from very small to 6 inches and more in diameter. Color range is also great. Some of the cultivated Maxillarias are very showy when well grown. The old groups *Camaridium* and *Ornithidium* are considered synonyms of *Maxillaria* by contemporary orchidologists.

Culture: Most of these plants should be grown—depending upon their place of origin—in the manner suggested for *Oncidium*. The dwarf, tuft-forming species need to be treated like *Ornithocephalus*. (C,I,H)

M. Camaridii (kam-ar-*id*-ee-eye)   (Guatemala to South America)

Pls. often pendulous and several feet long, the rhiz. usually closely covered with brownish papery bracts, the pbs. and infls. arising at scattered points. Lvs. 2 or 3 at each pb.-apex, to 1½' long, glossy dark green. Scapes to 2″ long, mostly produced in successive pairs from bract-axils of new growth. Fls. to 2½″ across, waxy, very fragrant of narcissus, seldom lasting more than one day, pure white, the inside of the lip vivid yellow, with reddish brown or reddish purple transverse lines. Mostly spring, flowering 3 or 4 times in successive flushes. (I,H)

M. luteo-alba (*loo*-tee-oh-*al*-bah)   (Costa Rica to Ecuador)

Pbs. clustered, rather flattened, shiny, to 4″ tall, with a solitary leathery, glossy lf. to 18″ long, dark green. Scapes several at once, to 6″ tall. Fls. very handsome, waxy, fragrant, lasting well, to 4″ across. Ss. Nankeen-yellow at tip, shading to almost white basally. Ps. smaller, similar in color or almost entirely yellow. Lip cream-white, streaked with dull purple on side lobes. Mostly winter—early spring. (I)

M. tenuifolia (ten-yoo-i-*foe*-lee-ah)   (Mexico to Nicaragua)

Pbs. round to egg-shaped, somewhat flattened, small, with brown bracts at base, borne at intervals from a creeping to almost erect rhiz. Lvs. grassy, ribbonlike, to 2' long. Scapes numerous, to 2″ long. Fls. about 1″ across, waxy, extremely fragrant of coconut, long-lived. Ss. and ps. dark red, spotted with bright or dull yellow. Lip vivid blood-red, yellowish at middle, spotted with red. Late winter—spring. (I,H)

MILTONIA
(mil-*tow*-nee-ah)

About 20 species of *Miltonia* are known, these being for the most part epiphytic orchids ranging from Costa Rica to Brazil, with most of them occurring in the Andes or in Brazil. This genus consists of two basic groups, those from high elevations being extremely popular with collectors (and being called, as an aggregation, the "Pansy Orchids," because of the shape and markings of the spectacular flowers), while the warmer-growing, mostly Brazilian species are only now making their appearance as common inhabitants of our greenhouses. The flowers of Miltonias are borne singly or in multiflorous racemes from the bases of the most recently formed pseudobulbs. In the Andean species they are usually white or pinkish, often with central blotches of vivid crimson or magenta, while in the Brazilian kinds they rather resemble certain types of *Odontoglossum*, a genus to which they are closely related; these have starlike segments, colored yellow or greenish, more or less barred or otherwise marked with brown, purple, or magenta-red.

CULTURE: Since the Miltonias occur from sea-level to very high in the chilly mountains of Colombia and Ecuador, two differing sets of cultural conditions are required for these orchids. The tropical species —mostly Brazilian in origin—thrive when grown in the manner suggested for *Oncidium*, while the alpine kinds—from the high mountains of the Andes—should be treated in the manner recommended for the high-elevation Odontoglossums. (C,I,H)

M. spectabilis (spek-*tah*-bi-liss) (Brazil)

Rhiz. robust, creeping, the flattened, usually yellowish green pbs. (to 4″ tall) produced at intervals, with paired lvs. Infls. erect, to about

FANTASTIC GARDENS VEITCH

Miltonia spectabilis var. *Moreliana* fma. *atro-rubens*

Miltonia vexillaria

8″ tall, 1-fld. Fls. almost flat, heavy-textured, to 3″ across, variable in color, the typical phase with white or cream-white ss. and ps., the lip wine-purple with 6–8 longitudinal veins of darker hue, the margins white or pale rose, very large, wavy-margined. July–Sept. (I,H)

var. **Moreliana** (mo-rel-ee-*ah*-nah)   (Brazil)

Distinctive variant, more commonly grown than the species, with fls. to 4″ across, the ss. and ps. plum-purple, the large flattened lip bright rose-purple with darker veins and reticulations. July–Sept. (I,H)

M. vexillaria (vex-il-*ah*-ree-ah)   (Colombia)

A popular species, with magnificent, variable fls. Pbs. clustered, grayish blue-green, to 4″ tall. Lvs. similar to pbs. in color, rather soft-textured. Infls. typically erect, often several at once from each pb., to 20″ tall, with 12 or more large, flattened, fragrant fls. to 3½″ long. Ss. and ps. usually pale rose-red or lilac-rose, sometimes all white or white with central blotches of vivid magenta. Lip 2½″ across, darker but generally similar in color to other parts, with a prominent yellow crest. Spring–early summer. (C)

MORMODES
(mor-*mow*-deez)

Commonly known as the "Goblin Orchids," about twenty species of *Mormodes* are known. They are all robust epiphytes or lithophytes in the American tropics, ranging from Mexico to Peru and Brazil. The plants closely resemble *Catasetum* and *Cycnoches,* but have perfect (that is, bisexual, or hermaphroditic) flowers, which are characterized by a twisted column and generally contorted floral segments. The species of *Mormodes* are not commonly cultivated, but the strange, frequently large and delightfully scented blossoms—found in combinations of lurid hues of purple, brown, green, and magenta, often with white—are sufficiently interesting to make their increased popularity justifiable.

Culture: As for *Catasetum.* (I,H)

M. Colossus (ko-*los*-us)   (Costa Rica; Panama)

Pbs. clustered, cylindric, to 1′ tall. Lvs. folded, large, eventually deciduous. Infls. to 2′ long, arching, usually rather many-fld. Fls. waxy, highly fragrant, to more than 3½″ in diam., contorted, the ss. and ps. olive-green, yellowish-brown, or cream, the lip (which has recurved margins) brown, tan, or yellow, narrowed at base. Spring. (I,H)

M. igneum (ig-*nee*-um)   (Costa Rica to Colombia)

Much like *M. Colossus* in habit, often more robust. Infls. 1-several per bulb, erect or arching, to more than 2′ long, few- to many-fld. Fls.

highly variable in size, color, and texture, fragrant, lasting well, to more than 2″ across, the ss. and ps. yellow, olive-green, tan-brown, or red, often spotted with red, the lip white, yellow, olive-green, tan, brown, or dark reddish brown, often with tiny brown or reddish brown spots. Lip almost round when spread out, sharply narrowed at base. Spring. (I,H)

Mormodes Colossus

GEORGE FULLER

NEOBENTHAMIA
(nee-oh-ben-*tham*-ee-ah)

The single species that makes up the genus *Neobenthamia* is an extremely handsome, tall-growing terrestrial orchid, native of the African island of Zanzibar and adjacent areas. The genus is placed by botanists rather near *Polystachya*. Although its cultural requirements are easily met, and it never fails to bloom, continuing over a period of several months when well established, it is today but rarely seen in our collections

CULTURE: As for *Sobralia*. Since it grows throughout the year, no rest-period should be afforded this handsome orchid. (H)

N. gracilis (gra-*si*-liss)   (Zanzibar, East Africa)

Graceful, clump-forming, to 6′ tall, the sts. bamboo-like, set with numerous grassy lvs. about 6″ long. Racs. terminal on the sts. (or on their branches), very dense, headlike. Fls. about ¾″ across, fragrant, waxy, long-lived. Ss. and ps. pure white. Lip white, with a central yellow stripe, on the sides of which some bright magenta spots typically occur. Mostly summer. (H)

NOTYLIA
(no-*til*-ee-ah)

This is a genus of about 40 species of seldom-seen but unusually interesting "botanical" orchids, epiphytes or lithophytes, which extend from Mexico to Bolivia and Brazil. *Notylia* is divided into two convenient sections, based on vegetative habit. One has small but distinct one-leaved pseudobulbs; the other has no pseudobulbs and has several fleshy leaves arranged in a small, basally overlapping fan, somewhat like a diminutive *Ornithocephalus* or *Oberonia*. The tiny but intricate flowers are borne either in tight clusters or in dense elongate racemes, and are usually found in white or in tones of greenish, yellow, or magenta. As yet the Notylias are little known save by connoisseur collectors, but they are enchanting little orchids, well deserving of attention by all hobbyists.

CULTURE: As for *Ornithocephalus*. Well-rooted specimens of *N. Barkeri* may be mounted on slabs of tree-fern fiber. They will thrive in brighter light than most other members of the genus. (I,H)

N. Barkeri (*bar*-ker-eye)   (Mexico to Panama)

Extremely variable in all parts. Pbs. clustered, oblong, glossy, to about 1″ long, with lf.-like basal bracts. Lf. (apical) solitary, leathery, glossy, to 7″ long. Infls. 1–several, usually sharply pendulous, very densely many-fld., to 1′ long at most. Fls. to ½″ long (usually smaller), faintly fragrant, white, sometimes yellow-spotted, complex in structure, the lip with a triangular apical part. Mostly spring. (I,H)

N. bicolor (*by*-kol-or)   (Mexico to Costa Rica)

Pbs. often absent, if present disc-shaped, flattened, very small. Lvs. in a superficial fan, leathery, sword-shaped, sharp-pointed, about 2″ long. Infls. pendulous, to 4″ long, densely many-fld. Fls. about ¾″ long, the ss. whitish, the ps. white spotted with dull purple, the lip whitish purple, with 2 darker spots on the disc. Summer. (I)

ODONTOGLOSSUM
(oh-don-toe-*gloss*-um)

Odontoglossum is an extremely diversified genus of upwards of 300 species, extending from Mexico to Bolivia and Brazil, with the majority of the known entities in the high Andean regions of South America. These justly popular orchids are variously epiphytic, lithophytic, or rarely terrestrial in the wild. Their generic alliance is with *Oncidium*,

Notylia bicolor

FOTO GÁLVEZ

Miltonia, Brassia, and the like. The inflorescences are produced from the base of the often prominent pseudobulbs and bear from one to several dozens of mostly rather large and spectacular flowers. These blossoms vary in color from pure glittering white (often spotted or blotched with other hues) through a series of yellow tones to chestnut-brown. A tremendous series of hybrids (including many made with the related genera noted above) is on record, and these include some of the finest of all cool-growing orchids.

CULTURE: Since the members of this genus range from hot lowlands to elevations higher than 10,000 feet, their cultural requirements vary markedly, according to the particular species—or individual specimen —under consideration. Those few Odontoglossums from low areas do best when treated like *Oncidium*. Those from high altitudes—comprising the bulk of the genus—require rather specialized treatment, and must be grown in the coolhouse for any degree of success to be obtained. In the wild, these alpine Odontoglossums are found in forests which are almost continuously bathed in fogs or chill rains, hence under cultivation conditions of constant moisture and high humidity, coupled with below-average temperatures, must be given. A perfectly drained compost is obviously necessary, and today most experts utilize a mixture of equal parts of chopped osmunda and chopped sphagnum moss, with a top-dressing of fresh green sphagnum moss. These cool-growing Odontoglossums should, unlike many other orchids, be underpotted; they flower with greater vigor when their roots are confined. Repotting and division (if necessary) should be attended to on an annual basis for best results. Because of the generally succulent foliage and soft pseudobulbs, a rather shaded spot is needed. All members of the genus benefit by frequent and rather liberal applications of fertilizing solution. (C,I,H)

O. crispum (*kriss*-pum)   (Colombia)

Among the finest and most variable of the spp., with many named forms. Pbs. egg-shaped, compressed, to 4″ tall. Lvs. 2 or 3, rather

VEITCH   GEORGE FULLER

Odontoglossum crispum   *Odontoglossum nobile*

soft-textured, narrow, to more than 1′ long. Infls. usually gracefully arching, rather densely many-fld., to 1½′ long. Fls. highly variable in size, color, and degree of crispness of segm.-margins, usually about 3″

across, mostly white or pale rose, sometimes more or less spotted and blotched with brownish or reddish brown. Lip usually white with a few red spots and a yellow center, the disc yellow streaked with brown or red-brown, rather heart-shaped. Mostly fall–winter. (C)

O. grande (*gran*-dee)   (Mexico; Guatemala)

Pbs. clustered, roundish, often rather compressed, dull green, to 4″ long and 2½″ broad. Lvs. 1–3, heavy-textured, stalked basally, to 1¼′ long and almost 3″ broad. Infls. 4–8-fld., usually erect, stout, to 1′ tall. Fls. widespreading, to more than 6″ across, waxy, long-lived, the ss. yellow with broad transverse bars and flecks of reddish brown, the ps. with the lower half reddish brown with yellow marginal marks, the upper half bright yellow, the smallish lip white or cream-white flecked with dull reddish brown. Fall–spring. (C,I)

O. pendulum (*pen*-doo-lum)   (Mexico)

Often grown under its synonym of *O. citrosmum*. Pbs. glossy, roundish, somewhat wrinkled with age, to 3″ tall. Lvs. 2, rather leathery, to 1′ long and 2½″ broad. Infls. sharply pendulous, produced from center of expanding new growths, 8–15-fld., with a long slender peduncle, to 1′ long. Fls. fragrant, waxy, long-lived, about 2″ across, variable in color, the typical phase white slightly flushed and sometimes dotted with pale blush-pink, the complex lip bright or pale mauve-pink with a pale or bright yellow basal claw, marginally wavy. Mostly fall. (C,I)

ONCIDIUM
(on-*sid*-ee-um)

Oncidium contains an estimated 750 different kinds of orchids, which are widespread in the Americas from South Florida and Mexico to Argentina. While in the wild they grow primarily as epiphytes, some occur in the ground and not a few exhibit a predilection for rock outcroppings. A large number of these plants are present in our collections today, and are often among our most highly prized and showy orchids. Vegetatively, Oncidiums are among the most diverse of all orchidaceous plants, but their flowers—generally yellow and brown in color—are relatively similar in superficial appearance. The form and tremendous quantities of these showy blossoms have earned the common names of "Dancing Ladies" and "Golden Showers" for this genus.

CULTURE: In a genus as large as this one, it is apparent that tremendous variance will be found in cultural requirements. Basic cultural necessities are much like those of *Cattleya*. The pendulous species of *Oncidium* must be planted on slabs of tree-fern fiber and exposed to virtually full sunlight at all times. Most other members of the genus do best in well-drained pots filled with a rather tightly packed compost of either straight osmunda fiber or a mixture of equal parts of chopped tree-fern fiber and dust-free bark preparation (with the addition of some chopped sphagnum moss for certain of the dwarf, rather delicate kinds). Perfect drainage is always essential for these orchids, which are highly intolerant of stale conditions at the roots. While actively growing, they delight in abundant water and—usually—high humidity, but in virtually all cases, upon completion of the new growths, a definite resting period of about 2 or 3 weeks' duration must be given for proper flower production. The plants require more direct sunlight than do most other orchids, and often will not bloom well without it. Otherwise they are mostly amenable to adverse conditions, and should form an integral part of even the smallest orchid collection. All Oncidiums benefit by frequent and liberal applications of fertilizer. (C,I,H)

O. luridum (*loo*-ri-dum)   (South Florida to Guianas and Peru)

Also known, perhaps more correctly, as *O. guttatum*. Lvs. very large, to 3′ long and 8″ broad, borne from tiny compressed pbs., leathery-fleshy, dark or light green, sometimes brown-spotted. Infls. to 12′ tall, arching or erect, more or less branched, with up to 400 fls. in tight clusters. Fls. to 1″ in diam., highly variable, slightly fragrant, typically yellowish green, densely covered with dark lustrous red-brown blotches, the segments with wavy margins. Summer. (I,H)

O. Papilio (pah-*pil*-ee-oh)   (Venezuela; Trinidad)

Pbs. roundish, flattened, wrinkled with age, blotched with red-brown. Lf. usually solitary, stiffly leathery, blotched, to 1′ long, shaded with purplish on underside. Infls. to 4′ tall, erect, slender, flattened on upper part, with several large showy fls. borne in succession over a lengthy period. Fls. about 4″ long, long-lasting. Dors. sep. and ps. erect, narrow, broad apically, red-brown, often with a few small yellow markings. Lat. ss. curved down, more or less around the lip, red-brown with irregular transverse yellow bars. Lip large, frilled, vivid yellow, with a red-brown front margin. Mostly summer, but sometimes almost everblooming. (I,H)

Oncidium Papilio

Oncidium varicosum var. *Rogersii*

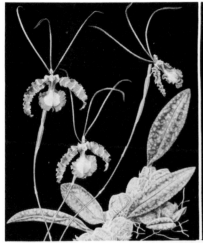

Oncidium Lanceanum

O. varicosum (vah-ri-*koe*-sum)   (Brazil)

A handsome and popular species, the size of the fls. variable. Pbs.
rather long-egg-shaped, furrowed, to 5" tall. Lvs. leathery, to 1' long.
Infls. mostly arching, to 6' long, branched, very many-fld. Fls. with
small, yellow, red-barred ss. and ps. at the base of a medium to large,
spreading, frilly, vivid yellow lip which often has a pale red-brown
suffusion on the basal crest, the lip to 2" across or more in var. *Rogersii*.
Fall–winter. (I)

ORNITHOCEPHALUS
(or-ni-tho-*sef*-ah-luss)

The 35 or so species of *Ornithocephalus* that are known are all small epiphytes of striking appearance ranging from Mexico to Trinidad and Brazil. Commonly known as "Bird's-Head Orchids," because of the shape of the tiny yet incredibly complex flowers, they are today reasonably frequent in choice collections. Without pseudobulbs, they have more or less fleshy foliage arranged in a tight, basally rooting fan, which somewhat resembles a diminutive iris rather than an orchid. The mostly green or white blossoms being in many species produced more than once annually adds to their value for the hobbyist.

CULTURE: The cultural requirements of *Ornithocephalus* are basically those under which a great many of the smaller "botanical" orchids thrive. In nature, the leaf-fans of this genus are frequently pendulous, but in our collections they do well when grown upright, in small, perfectly drained pots in a tightly packed compost made up of about equal parts of chopped sphagnum moss, chopped tree-fern fiber, and tiny bits of dust-free bark preparation. A top-dressing of fresh sphagnum moss is recommended for moisture-retention purposes, since these plants have no water-storing structures such as pseudobulbs. They must never be permitted to dry out, and yet sodden conditions at the roots will rapidly prove fatal to their rather delicate constitutions. Shade is necessary to avoid burning of the succulent foliage, and periodic applications of a weakened fertilizing solution seem most beneficial. Warm or at least intermediate temperatures are suggested, since these are all tropical orchids. (I,H)

O. bicornis (by-*kor*-niss) (Guatemala to Panama)

Lvs. grayish green, forming a fan, rigid, 1¾–3½" long. Infls. racemose, slender, few-to many-fld., fuzzy, with large bracts. Fls. cupshaped, rather long-lived, to about 3/16" in diam., the ss. and ps. greenish white or greenish yellow, the lip green at its fleshy base. Mostly winter. (I,H)

O. inflexus (in-*flex*-uss) (Mexico and British Honduras to Panama)

Lvs. dull or bright green, forming a fan, often rather soft-textured, to 4" long, the basal sheaths almost transparent. Infls. slender, racemose, often rather zigzag, smooth, loosely many-fld. from the base, to more than 3" long. Fls. to about 3/16" in diam., whitish green or greenish, sometimes with some darker green markings on the essentially entire lip. Winter. (I,H)

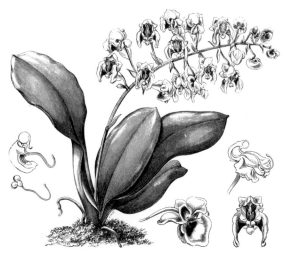

Ornithocephalus grandiflorus

VEITCH

PAPHIOPEDILUM
(paf-ee-oh-*ped*-i-lum)

While about 50 species of *Paphiopedilum* are known, the genus is most remarkable for its many handsome and tremendously popular hybrids. In nature the plants are terrestrial, lithophytic, or rather rarely epiphytic. The genus is widespread over a large region extending from China and the Himalayas throughout Southeast Asia and Indonesia to New Guinea. Its members being commonly called "Lady's-Slippers," they are confusingly known by many orchidists under the name *Cypripedium*, which applies to a totally distinct group of this alliance. Many thousands of artificially induced hybrids have been made in this genus, and these form an important part of even the smallest collection of orchids today.

CULTURE: Paphiopedilums are generally best grown in well-drained pots, in a wide variety of media, though perhaps the most popular is a mixture of about equal parts of chopped osmunda and chopped sphagnum moss, often with the addition of a small amount of fibrous loam and/or gritty white sand. Many authorities advocate the addition of a top-dressing of fresh, green, actively-growing sphagnum. These orchids must never be allowed to become dry at the roots, and in general they do best in a greenhouse in which the high humidity they need can be maintained. Generally, they require semishaded exposure, although excessive shade will reduce flower production. Weakened fertilizer solutions may be applied at frequent intervals to good advantage. Temperature requirements vary, although the vast majority of the currently grown species and hybrids do best under relatively cool conditions. (C,I,H)

P. barbatum (bar-*bah*-tum)　　　　　　(Thailand; Malay Peninsula)

Lvs. tongue-shaped, blunt at tip, to 6″ long and slightly more than 1″ wide, with rather dark green checkerings. Scape 1-fld., to 10″ tall.

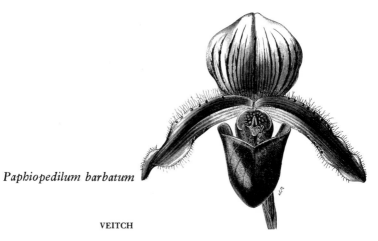

Paphiopedilum barbatum

VEITCH

Fls. about 4″ across, sometimes smaller. Dors. sep. almost circular, whitish or pale green toward base, with dark brown-red longitudinal nerves. Ps. sharply turned downward, purple toward the greenish base, with scattered, almost black warts. Lip purple-brown, the incurved side lobes with small purplish warts and spots. Spring–fall. (I,H)

P. callosum (kal-*oh*-sum)　　　　　　(Thailand; Indochina)

Lvs. few (usually only 4 or 5), to 10″ long, to almost 2″ broad, rather rigid, the upper side light bluish green with darker mottling. Scape 1-fld., to 1¼′ tall. Fls. about 4″ in diam., very showy and long-lived, somewhat variable in color. Dors. sep. almost circular, white, with 11–13 longitudinal purple streaks. Ps. sharply deflected downward, greenish at base, becoming suffused with purplish near the apex. Lip rather large, brown-purple. Mostly spring–summer. (I,H)

P. insigne (in-*sig*-nee)　　　　　　(Himalayas)

Lvs. 5 or 6, rather narrow, 8–12″ long and to 1″ broad, of a uniform, usually pale green. Scape 1-fld., to about 1′ tall. Fls. 4–5″ in diam., highly variable in color, of a varnished appearance. Dors. sep. broadly oval, the median and basal area apple-green with numerous brownish purple spots arranged with more or less regularity along the longitudinal green veins, the apical area white. Synsepal smaller, pale green. Ps. spreading, wavy-margined, pale yellowish green with brownish purple longitudinal veins. Lip helmet-shaped, yellowish green shaded with brown, the infolded lobes dark tawny yellow. There are a great many named horticultural variants. Fall–spring. (C,I)

PERISTERIA
(per-iss-*ter*-ee-ah)

This genus of about 6 species of variously epiphytic or terrestrial orchids is of importance primarily because it includes the fabulous "Holy Ghost Orchid," *Peristeria elata*, the national flower of the Republic of Panama. Several other members of this genus deserve to be known, for they are spectacular epiphytic plants much like *Acineta*. The range of *Peristeria* extends from Costa Rica to Surinam, Brazil, and Peru.

CULTURE: *P. elata* requires rather specialized conditions in order to induce flowering. In the wild, this spectacular orchid typically inhabits heavily shaded to semi-sunny areas on the borders of wooded tracts, the plants resting on a thick layer of rotted leaves, with the roots scarcely penetrating into the clayey ground underneath. A loose, well-aerated compost is thus required in our collections; one made up of equal parts of leaf-mold and rich humus, with the addition of some chopped tree-fern fiber and a small amount of chunks of bark preparation, liberally interspersed with broken crock, is suitable, with at least half of the pot filled with crock to assist in drainage. Abundant water should be given while the plants are actively growing, but upon maturation of the new pseudobulbs, moisture should be strictly curtailed until root-action again commences. Warm temperatures should prevail with this species, and likewise with all of the other Peristerias, which require the conditions suggested for *Acineta*. Periodic heavy feedings are beneficial to all members of this group, and the plants should be disturbed as infrequently as possible. (I,H)

P. elata (ee-*lah*-tah)   (Costa Rica to Venezuela)

Terrestrial or very rarely epiphytic species, popular in cultivation. Pbs. eggshaped, shiny, robust, to 7″ tall and 4″ in diameter, clustered. Lvs.

deciduous in time, stalked, folded, to 5′ tall, mostly erect. Infls. stiffly erect, to 6′ tall, with up to 20 handsome, fragrant fls toward the apex, opening in succession over a long period. Fls. rounded, cuplike, fleshy, about 2″ across in large phases, heavily candy-scented, complex in structure, waxen-white, the intricate lip usually with some tiny purple dots and a faint lilac suffusion. Summer–fall. (I,H)

PESCATOREA
(pess-kah-*toe*-ree-ah)

The genus *Pescatorea* consists of about a dozen spectacular, bulbless epiphytes, native in the region extending from Costa Rica to Colombia and Ecuador; regrettably, only one of these is to be found in our collections today, and this is a very rare orchid. Allied to *Huntleya* and *Chondrorhyncha*, they resemble those plants vegetatively, and, like them, bear large, waxen, fragrant, solitary blossoms on short basal scapes. These blossoms are long-lasting and frequently are produced in great abundance.

CULTURE: As for *Huntleya*. (C,I)

P. cerina (seh-*ree*-nah)   (Costa Rica; Panama)

Without pbs., the plants consisting of rather clustered tufts of erect lvs. arranged in a loose fan. Lvs. usually relatively rigid, glossy, to 2′

Pescatorea cerina

H. A. DUNN

long and 3″ broad. Scapes basal, horizontal to erect, to 4″ long. Fls. to 3″ across, waxy, heavily fragrant, the ss. and ps. white (the lat. ss.

generally with a greenish yellow blotch at base), the lip vivid yellow, with a very large and fleshy callus which may be sparsely marked with reddish brown. Fall. (C,I)

PHAIUS
(*fay*-uss)

Almost 30 different species of *Phaius* are known, most of which are large and showy terrestrial plants, but only a few of them are in contemporary cultivation. The genus ranges from East Africa and Malagasy (Madagascar) throughout Tropical Asia and Indonesia to the Himalayas, New Caledonia, and the Fiji Islands. Pseudobulbous plants, they have large folded leaves which are eventually deciduous, and erect spikes of often sizable, peculiarly-colored, but lovely flowers.

CULTURE: Plants of Phaius do best in large well-drained pots, in a compost of about one-third rich loam, one-third well-rotted manure, and one-sixth each shredded osmunda and tree-fern fiber. Fertilizer should be added at regular and frequent intervals, for these orchids are heavy feeders. Upon completion of the new growths, a rest-period of about 3 weeks should be afforded. While Phaius demand a brightly lighted spot, care must be taken that the rather thin foliage does not burn. Temperatures should be high at all times for best results, though the popular *P. Tankervilliae* will often withstand exposure to about 40° F. for brief periods without serious injury. (I,H)

P. Tankervilliae (tank-er-*vil*-ee-eye)   (Tropical Asia and Indonesia)

Common synonyms are *P. grandifolius* and *P. Wallichii*. Pbs. tightly clustered, rather irregular, dull green, to about 3″ high. Lvs. 3 or 4, to 3′ long, folded, rather heavy. Infls. stout, borne from the pb.-base, to more than 4′ tall, 10–20-fld., with large deciduous bracts. Fls. fragrant, heavy-textured, long-lived, to 4½″ across, the ss. and ps. powdery white outside, more or less red-brown inside, often with yellowish margins, the large tubular lip mostly whitish outside, the blade dark wine-red inside, purplish apically and somewhat so at base. This attractive orchid is naturalized in Cuba, Jamaica, Panama, and Hawaii. Mostly spring. (I,H)

PHALAENOPSIS
(fal-eye-*nop*-siss)

The fabulous "Moth Orchids"—as members of the genus *Phalaenopsis* are commonly called—are today extremely popular both with hobbyists and with commercial growers. The number of hybrids is astronomical, and many kinds are grown in great quantities for the cut-flower trade, the white forms being especially valued for wedding bouquets. About 70 species are known, with a range extending from the Himalayas through Malaysia to Indonesia, and from Formosa through the Philippines to New Guinea and Queensland. Mostly epiphytic in the wild, they have a characteristic appearance—short stems bearing only a few leathery leaves that are often huge. The inflorescences, set with one to several dozen intricate, spectacular flowers, mostly of long-lasting qualities, are sometimes abbreviated, sometimes elongate.

CULTURE: Phalaenopsis is, almost entirely, a tropical group of orchids; hence the plants require warm temperatures at all times. Since they possess no pseudobulbs and grow throughout the year, they must never be permitted to become dry; yet the compost in which they are kept must be sufficiently porous to assure perfect and rapid drainage. Most experts advocate a compost of firmly packed osmunda fiber, though others use various mixtures of tree-fern and bark preparation. Ideally, these shade-loving plants should be kept in the warm greenhouse, and provided with the constant moisture and high humidity in which they thrive. Excessive sun will burn the succulent foliage. While in especially active growth, plants of Phalaenopsis benefit by liberal and regular applications of fertilizers, preferably liquid. (I,H)

Phaius Tankervilliae

REVEREND N. E. G.
CRUTTWELL

P. amabilis (ah-*mab*-i-liss)   (Indonesia to N. Australia)

Lvs. few, rather fleshy and leathery, blunt at tip, dull green above and below, to more than 1′ long and about 5″ broad. Infls. slender, gracefully arching, to 3′ long, usually loosely 6–20-fld. Fls. to 4″ across, variable in size and in dimensions of segments, white, flushed with yellow on the intricate lip and more or less marked and striped with red around the basal lip-calli. Mostly Oct.–Jan. (I,H)

P. Lueddemanniana (loo-ed-ee-man-ee-*ah*-nah)   (Philippines)

Lvs. few, bright waxy yellowish green, rather rigid, to 10" long and 5" broad. Infls. usually not longer than the lvs., irregularly zigzag, 2–7-fld., the fls. usually produced singly over a long period. Fls. variable in size and color, mostly less than 2" in diam., highly fragrant and long-lived, waxy, iridescent in most forms, in the typical phase with the ss. chestnut-brown with some rather narrow, pale yellow streaks, the margins whitish and the basal half heavily suffused with amethyst; ps. smaller than ss., mostly bright amethyst with more scattered chestnut-brown streaks, the margins whitish. Lip 3-lbd., white, magenta and yellow, with numerous erect, bristle-like, white hairs on the median keel. Spring. (I,H)

P. Schilleriana (shil-er-ee-*ah*-nah)   (Philippines)

Vegetatively rather similar to *P. amabilis*, but the lvs. usually softer and dull dark green mottled with silver-gray, often magenta underneath. Infls. erect to gracefully arching, to more than 3' long, few- to many-fld., usually branched. Fls. variable in size, often not lasting well, usually less than 2½" across, fragrant, generally pale pinkish rose, the disc of the intricate lip golden-yellow marked with scarlet, the basal part of the midlb. red-dotted. Mostly spring. (I,H)

PHOLIDOTA
(fol-i-*doe*-tah)

This genus, which is rather closely related to *Coelogyne*—differing from it only in certain technical floral details—contains about 40 species of primarily epiphytic orchids which are found over an extensive area from the Himalayas and southern China to New Caledonia. Vegetatively resembling many of the Coelogynes, most Pholidotas are characterized by the proportionately large, often overlapping, papery bracts of the inflorescence, which gives the common name of "Rattlesnake Orchid" to several of the species, notably *P. imbricata*. The individual flowers are generally small in size and of rather dull hue, but their extraordinary mode of placement on the inflorescence and the freedom with which they are produced makes them of interest to all orchidists.
CULTURE: As for *Coelogyne*. (C,I,H)

P. imbricata (im-bri-*kah*-tah)   (S. E. Asia; Indonesia, etc.)

Pbs. clustered, elongate-egg-shaped, to 4″ tall, each with a single rigidly fleshy lf. to about 1′ long, stalked basally. Infls. arising with the new growths, gradually elongating so that they hang downward, the naked stalk to 1′ long, the rac. almost as long, very dense, with prom-

Pholidota imbricata

REG S. DAVIS

inent, overlapping, papery, brownish bracts. Fls. less than ½″ across, rather musk-scented, varying from whitish or cream-colored to tan, the lip usually marked with dull orange-brown. Mostly spring–summer. (I,H)

PHRAGMIPEDIUM
(frag-mi-*pee*-dee-um)

The 12 or so species of *Phragmipedium* that are known to date are mostly handsome and justifiably popular orchids. Mainly terrestrial, or rarely lithophytic or epiphytic orchids they range from southern Mexico (Chiapas) to Peru, Bolivia, and Brazil. The group is unfortunately usually known under the erroneous name *Selenipedium* (which applies to a completely different genus of "Lady's-Slippers," none of which are in cultivation at this time), or even as *Cypripedium*. Certain forms of the widespread *P. caudatum* produce flowers among the largest known in the orchid family, and because of their structure are called "Mandarin Orchids."

CULTURE: As for *Paphiopedilum*. (I,H)

P. caudatum (kaw-*dah*-tum)   (S. Mexico to Ecuador and Peru)

Lvs. arranged in clustered fans, tongue-shaped, rather rigidly leathery, to 2' long and more than 2" broad, often rather yellowish green. Infls. erect, to more than 2' tall, very loosely 1–6-fld. in upper parts. Fls. to more than 2½' long. Dors. sep. 6–7" long, pale yellow or whitish with longitudinal yellow-green veins in front. Ps. narrow, ribbonlike, pendulous, elongating, as the fl. expands, to more than 2' long (rarely

Phragmipedium caudatum

H. A. DUNN

to more than 30"), yellowish basally, otherwise dull brownish crimson. Lip slipper-shaped, brownish green passing to bronze-green around the orifice, the veins and reticulations dark green, pale yellow-green beneath, the infolded lobes ivory-white spotted with purple inside the yellow-brown border around the orifice. Spring–fall. (I)

P. longifolium (lon-ji-*foe*-lee-um)   (Costa Rica to Colombia)

Lf.-tufts close together, lvs. rather thin, narrow, to 2¾' long and 1½" broad, usually rather dark but bright green. Infls. erect, stout, dark purple or green, 6–10-fld. or more, the fls. usually produced singly over a long period. Fls. waxy, long-lasting, to almost 8" in diam., not as long. Dors. sep. mostly erect or somewhat thrust forward, pale green with rose veins and whitish margins. Synsepal very large, pale green with darker veins. Ps. spreading almost horizontally, narrow, often slightly twisted, pale yellow-green with rose margins, these margins becoming whitish basally. Lip slipper-shaped, yellow-green tinged with brown in front, the infolded lobes yellow-green dotted with rose-purple. Mostly fall, but occasionally more than once annually. (I)

PLEIONE
(plee-*yoh*-nee)

Pleione contains an estimated 20 species of very showy, terrestrial, lithophytic, or rarely epiphytic orchids, often included in *Coelogyne*, native in China, the Himalayas, Southeast Asia, and Formosa, several of which appear in choice collections. They possess rather squat, often angular pseudobulbs, topped by a few rather folded leaves, and give rise to large, solitary blossoms of great beauty and delicacy. Many of these fine orchids appear to be almost completely hardy—inhabiting regions in which they are sometimes covered by snow—hence should be more popular with enthusiasts in cool climates. Spreading sepals and petals surround a tubular, very handsome lip which is usually furnished with numerous complex teeth and calli.

CULTURE: Pleiones require rather specialized cultural conditions, being best treated as terrestrial plants much in the manner of *Phaius*. After flowering, the bulbs should be separated and replanted individually, spaced an inch or two apart in shallow fern-pans or pots, in a rich compost made up of leaf-mould, chopped osmunda fiber, chopped sphagnum-moss, and sharp white sand, mixed in about equal parts. Perfect drainage is most essential for success with this genus. Water should be given very sparingly until the roots are actively growing; then it may be applied copiously. When the new pseudobulbs are mature, moisture should be withheld almost completely, giving only enough to prevent excessive shriveling. A fresh, airy, rather sunny spot suits them well. Fertilizer can with benefit be applied while the plants are growing. Most of the cultivated Pleiones come from rather high elevations, hence cool temperatures are required. (C,I)

P. humilis (*hoo*-mi-liss)   (Himalayas)

Pbs. egg-shaped, narrowed above, to 3″ tall. Lf. solitary, to 6″ long, folded, deciduous. Fls. solitary, often several produced from each growth, to almost 5″ in diam., sweetly fragrant, the ss. and ps. white, the lip tubular, white, veined with golden-yellow on the front, the margin with some red dots, the tube spotted with violet-purple. Winter. (C)

P. maculata (mah-kyoo-*lah*-tah)   (Himalayas)

Pbs. flask-shaped or almost conical, rather compressed in age. Lvs. usually 2, to 5" long, folded, deciduous. Fls. solitary, fragrant, about 4" in diam., white, the ss. and ps. streaked with purple, the lip white or rose, with some dark red blotches on the margin, the base of the tube yellow. Winter. (C,I)

P. praecox (*pry*-kox)   (Himalayas)

Pbs. egg-shaped, about 3" tall. Lvs. 2, to 1' long, folded, deciduous. Fls. solitary, about 5" across, fragrant, long-lasting, the ss. and ps.

DONALD F. MERRETT

Pleione formosana

magenta-red. Lip tubular, dark magenta-red, set with white and golden-yellow keels in the tube. Winter. (C,I)

PLEUROTHALLIS
(ploo-row-*thal*-iss)

Pleurothallis is without a doubt the largest genus of the Orchidaceae in the New World, with as many as 1,000 species being recognized; yet it is virtually unknown by the average contemporary hobbyist. The reason is that these are strictly "botanical" orchids, often very dwarf in stature, and generally producing extremely small—but fascinatingly intricate—blossoms. With the recent augmented interest in these miniatures, however, some of the myriad species of *Pleurothallis* are coming into our collections, and a great many more of them should become better known. The group ranges from South Florida and Mexico to Argentina, with the greatest number of species occurring in Brazil, the Colombian Andes, and in Costa Rica. Principally epiphytic in habit, they are strange, pseudobulbless plants with highly variable vegetative growth, and usually erect or arching racemes of vaguely bell-shaped, multihued blossoms which are jewel-like in appearance when studied under a magnifying lens.

W. M. BUSWELL
Pleurothallis gelida

T. MAC DOUGALL
Pleurothallis Grobyi

CULTURE: Most species of *Pleurothallis* do well when given the cultural conditions suggested for *Ornithocephalus*, though the numerous high-elevation inhabitants of the "cloud forest" regions should be grown like the alpine Masdevallias. (C,I,H)

P. Ghiesbreghtiana (geez-brek-tee-*ah*-nah)

(West Indies; Mexico to Panama)

Pls. slender, clustered, 4½–24″ tall, highly variable in all parts. Sts. 1½–7″ tall. Lf. solitary, rigidly leathery, paddle-shaped to narrow, glossy bright green, to almost 7″ long, to 1¼″ broad. Infl. solitary, sheathed at base, furnished with several tubular bracts, loosely many-fld., slender, to about 15″ tall. Fls. nodding, fragrant, long-lasting, about

¼–½" long, translucent, yellow or greenish yellow, the lat. ss. united almost their entire length. Mostly winter. (I,H)

P. Grobyi (*grow*-bee-eye)

(West Indies; Mexico to N. South America)

Pls. extremely variable, mat- or cluster-forming, 1¼–6" tall, the sts. almost obsolete. Lf. rigidly leathery, usually roundish, mostly purplish underneath, ¼–3" long. Infls. erect, threadlike, loosely few-fld., somewhat zigzag, 1–6" tall. Fls. not opening fully, often nodding, to more than ¼" long, greenish white or yellow, marked (often striped longitudinally) with reddish purple, the lat. ss. united to form a 2-toothed lamina. Spring–summer. (I,H)

POLYRRHIZA
(pol-ee-*ry*e-zah)

This is a remarkable genus of 4 species, natives of South Florida and the West Indies, all epiphytes in the wild, and today extremely scarce in our collections. Vaguely allied to *Angraecum*, *Polyrrhiza* contains some of the most spectacular of the weird leafless orchids, in which the plants consist merely of an abbreviated perennial rhizomelike stem, a tangled cluster of grayish roots (which carry on the processes of photosynthesis for the organism), and inflorescences. The flowers are sufficiently large to warrant their cultivation by specialized collectors.

CULTURE: Ideally, these odd epiphytes should be grown on the original trees or branches on which they occur in the wild, since their transferral to any artificial apparatus is a tedious and often discouragingly difficult matter. On some occasions, though, they have been successfully transplanted onto slabs of tree-fern fiber, with the brittle, sprawling roots tightly affixed against the medium until they take hold. Because they require extremely high humidity, abundant water at all times, and warm temperatures, they must be kept in the tropical greenhouse. Shade is essential, and it has been found that periodic applications of weakened fertilizer solution prove beneficial. (H)

P. Lindeni (*lin*-den-eye)　　　　　　　　(South Florida; Cuba)

Pls. leafless, the sts. very reduced, emitting long (to 6′), flexuous, gray-green roots. Infls. rather stout, brownish-black, 2½–9" long, producing several fls. which open successively. Fls. showy, fragrant, waxy, long-lived, to almost 5" long from tip to tip, the dors. sep. and ps. reflexed, white more or less flushed with cream-yellow or green, the lat. ss. curving down, then outward, similar in color. Lip very large and complex, pure white, boat-shaped at base, the midlb. suddenly dilated into a pair of long antenna-like lbs. which spread outward, then downward, and end in curly tips. Feb.–July. (H)

Polyrrhiza Lindeni

DRAWING BY BLANCHE AMES

POLYSTACHYA
(pol-i-*stak*-ee-ah)

The distribution of the more than 130 known species of *Polystachya* is an unusual one: while most of them occur in Tropical Africa, the genus also extends into the Americas and Asia. As yet little known by collectors, these are highly variable plants—primarily epiphytic or lithophytic in habit—with small to medium-sized, mostly numerous flowers of a characteristic hooded shape, occurring in a tremendous range of color combinations.

CULTURE: As for *Dendrobium*, depending upon the place of origin of the particular species or individual. (I,H)

P. affinis (af-*in*-is) (Sierra Leone to Belgian Congo)

Pbs. almost disc-shaped, flattened strongly from above, usually flushed with purplish, very close together, to 2″ in diam. Lvs. 2, borne from middle of pb.-apex, leathery, to 8″ long, the undersurface usually purple. Infls. arching to sharply pendulous, loosely many-fld., to 1′ long, densely covered with short, mostly orange hairs. Fls. cup-shaped, covered outside with short orange hairs, about ½″ across, golden

yellow or orange-yellow, more or less striped with brown. July–Aug.
(H)

Polystachya obanensis

GEORGE FULLER

RENANTHERA
(ren-an-*theh*-rah)

The dozen known species of *Renanthera* are variously epiphytic,
lithophytic, or terrestrial in habit. Today they are relatively popular
with collectors because of their great sprays of spectacular, usually
scarlet blossoms. The range of the genus extends from China and the
Himalayas throughout Southeast Asia, the Philippines, and Indonesia
to New Guinea. Mostly vinelike, some of them resemble smallish
Vandas, while others are huge plants many feet tall, with the leaves
expanding several feet across. Some splendid hybrids are known with
certain of the allied genera of the *Vanda* alliance.

CULTURE: As for *Vanda* and *Arachnis*, depending upon the size of
the species under consideration. Full sun-exposure is usually needed by
all members of this genus for proper flower production. (I,H)

R. coccinea (kok-*sin*-ee-ah)　　　　(South China to Thailand)

Sts. clambering, usually erect, freely rooting, to 15′ tall. Lvs. numerous, horizontally spreading, rigidly leathery, usually yellowish green,
4–6″ long. Infls. to 4′ long, produced from the st. opposite one of
the upper lvs., usually branched and in some instances bearing more
than 150 fls. Fls. about 3½″ long, long-lasting, changing in color as

they age, the dors. sep. and ps. vivid red spotted with yellow, the ps. slightly narrower and shorter; lat. ss. dark vermilion, glossy, sharply narrowed at base; lip small, intricate, red and yellow. Spring–fall. (H)

R. Imschootiana (im-shoo-tee-*ah*-nah)   (Assam; Indochina)

St. usually solitary, usually less than 3′ tall, densely leafy. Lvs. fleshy, rather rigid, dark green, usually less than 4″ long and ¾″ broad. Infls. horizontally spreading, branched, rather loosely many-fld., to 1½′ long.

GEORGE FULLER

Renanthera Imschootiana

Fls. to more than 2¼″ long, lasting more than a month, the dors. sep. and ps. narrow, yellow, the ps. mostly spotted with scarlet, the lat. ss. larger, narrowed basally, light red or vivid scarlet; lip small, scarlet, with yellow keels. Summer, especially June–July. (I)

RHYNCHOLAELIA
(rin-koe-*ly*e-lee-ah)

The 2 known species of *Rhyncholaelia* are both relatively frequent in collections at this time, being almost universally known as *Brassavola*, in which genus they were formerly included. In the wild, they usually inhabit smallish trees in relatively dry regions in Mexico and Central

America. Both species—particularly *R. Digbyana*—have been used to a tremendous extent in the production of hybrids with *Cattleya* and other allied groups. These fine, spectacular forms are still known horticulturally as Brassocattleyas, Brassolaeliocattleyas, etc.

CULTURE: These marvelous orchids require the general cultural conditions that are afforded Cattleyas. They rebel at overly moist conditions, and a perfectly drained medium—preferably tightly-packed osmunda—is recommended. Copious applications of fertilizer have proved to be beneficial. The plants should be kept in as much bright sun as the specimens will tolerate short of burning. (I,H)

R. Digbyana (dig-bee-*ah*-nah)   (Mexico to Honduras)

Usually known as *Brassavola Digbyana*. Pbs. club-shaped, compressed, concealed by whitish sheaths, to 8″ tall, grayish. Lf. solitary, rigidly fleshy, grayish green, to 8″ long and more than 2″ wide. Infls. 1-fld., terminal, with a large spathelike sheath. Fls. extremely fragrant (especially at night), long-lived, heavy-textured, glossy, to almost 7″ across, pale yellowish green, the huge lip usually cream-white, more or less flushed with greenish, often with a vivid emerald-green area in the throat. Lip with apical margins intricately fringed. Spring–summer. (I,H)

R. glauca (*glaw*-kah)   (Mexico to Honduras)

Pbs. oblong-spindle-shaped, not overly close together on the creeping rhiz., grayish, to 4″ long. Lf. solitary, rigidly leathery, powdery-grayish, to 4½″ long and 1¼″ broad. Infls. 1-fld., with a large compressed spathelike sheath. Fls. to almost 5″ across, heavy-textured, fragrant at night, long-lived, olive-green to white or palest lavender (the ps. usually very pale), the large flaring lip white or pale cream-white with a rose-pink spot or several reddish stripes in the throat. Late winter–spring. (I,H)

RHYNCHOSTYLIS
(rin-koe-*sty*-liss)

Four species of *Rhynchostylis* are known, 2 of which are relatively frequent in choice collections, where they are often known as "Fox-tail Orchids," in allusion to the tremendous brushlike racemes of lovely, colorful flowers. These are husky epiphytic plants indigenous to the Indo-Malaysian and Philippine area, allies of *Vanda*, and of rather facile culture.

Culture: Generally as for *Vanda*. These spectacular orchids are extremely intolerant of being disturbed, hence when the compost requires changing, it should—if at all possible—be carefully teased out from around the roots, and replaced in like fashion, rather than completely removing the specimen from its original container. (I,H)

R. gigantea (jie-*gan*-tee-ah)　　　　　　　　　(Burma; Thailand)

Usually grown under its synonym, *Saccolabium giganteum*. Sts. stout, usually less than 4″ tall, producing numerous very heavy roots. Lvs. very heavy, tongue-shaped, to 1′ long and 2¼″ broad. Infls. to 1¼′ long, pendulous, very densely many-fld. Fls. waxy, long-lasting, highly fragrant, about 1″ in diam., the ss. and ps. pure white more or less spotted with red-violet or magenta, often with a well-defined apical blotch of this color, the lip red-violet or magenta, usually whitish toward the middle and base. Fall–early winter. (I,H)

R. retusa (reh-*too*-sah)　　　　　　(India and Ceylon to Philippines)

Usually grown as *Saccolabium retusum* or *S. Blumei*. St. robust, to 2′ tall, emitting numerous stout roots. Lvs. tongue-shaped, close to-

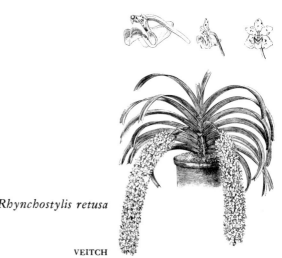

Rhynchostylis retusa

VEITCH

gether, heavy-textured, to more than 1′ long, often with pale longitudinal streaks on both surfaces. Infls. pendulous, to 2′ long, typically very densely many-fld. and cylindrical. Fls. fragrant, waxy, short- or long-lived, variable in color, about ¾″ across, the ss. and ps. white more or less copiously spotted with amethyst-purple, the lip entirely amethyst-purple. Summer–fall. (I,H)

RODRIGUEZIA
(rod-ri-*gwee*-zee-ah)

Rodriguezia is a genus of about 30 species of attractive epiphytic or lithophytic orchids in the Americas, ranging from Costa Rica to Peru and Brazil. Mostly small plants with rather prominent pseudobulbs, some of them form tufts while others have amazingly elongate, wire-like rhizomes. One or more arching, dense racemes are borne on each growth, set with intricate blossoms which occur in a wide range of color. As yet, Rodriguezias are uncommon in our collections, although the group includes some of the most cheerily showy of all small-growing orchids.

CULTURE: Rodriguezias may be grown with facility either in pots or baskets, or—once the root-systems are active—on rafts or slabs. A perfectly drained compost, usually of osmunda or tree-fern fiber, is used, since these orchids are highly intolerant of stale conditions. While in active growth they benefit by copious supplies of water, and flourish in bright light under warm or intermediate temperatures. Since they mostly grow without cessation, little or no rest need be given them upon completion of the new pseudobulbs. Applications of fertilizer prove beneficial with all of these orchids. (I,H)

R. secunda (se-*kun*-dah)   (Panama to Brazil)

Pbs. compressed, clustered, about 1½" long, dark green, subtended

Rodriguezia secunda

FANTASTIC GARDENS

by large lf.-like bracts. Lvs. several, usually rigidly leathery, dark green, to 9½" long. Infls. 1–6 per growth, erect or gracefully arching, to as much as 1' long, densely many-fld., the fls. all facing upward. Fls. about 1" long in largest phases, varying from almost white through several shades of pink to brilliant rose-red, the ss. and ps. forming a hood over the wavy-margined lip. Mostly winter–spring. (I,H)

R. venusta (ven-*oos*-tah)   (Brazil; Peru)

Rather similar in habit to *R. secunda*. Infls. loosely few-fld., arching, to 7" long. Fls. about 1½" long, very fragrant, white with a vivid golden-yellow disc on the fan-shaped lip. Fall. (I,H)

SCAPHYGLOTTIS
(skaf-ee-*glaw*-tiss)

Although *Scaphyglottis* contains some of the most unusual of all the "botanical" orchids, few of the more than 50 species are ever encountered in cultivation. Largely epiphytic (rarely lithophytic) in habit, they range from Mexico and the West Indies throughout Central America to Bolivia and southern Brazil. Extremely diverse in vegetative structure, they customarily produce a wealth of diminutive blossoms in a wide range of hues and with an intricate structure that must be examined with a magnifying lens to be appreciated. Many species of *Scaphyglottis* have a peculiar growth habit, with the slender or spindle-shaped pseudobulbs borne one on top of the other, forming a complex mass.

CULTURE: As for *Ornithocephalus*. (C,I,H)

S. Behrii (*bear*-ee-eye)   (Guatemala to Colombia)

Pls. often pendulous, forming dense clumps, the pbs. rather slender, stalked, superposed one above the other or in small tufts, 2–8" long. Lvs. 2, grasslike, 3–11" long, often very thin-textured. Fls. less than ¼" across, borne in clusters at apex of each successive pb., not opening fully, white, the lip larger than other segments, 3-lbd. above the middle, sometimes faintly flushed with pale lilac. Mostly spring. (I,H)

SCUTICARIA
(skoo-ti-*kah*-ree-ah)

Only 2 of the 3 known species of *Scuticaria* are as yet in cultivation. These most unusual epiphytic orchids, somewhat allied to *Maxillaria*, are indigenous to Brazil, the Guianas, and Venzeuela. They bear large and showy flowers at the base of whiplike leaves which hang in odd clumps sometimes more than 4 feet long from their host trees. (In the one species not yet cultivated the leaves are erect.)

CULTURE: Because of the pendulous habit of the species described below, these orchids must be grown on rafts or in baskets hung sideways. They do best in a tightly packed compost of osmunda or tree-fern fiber, and should be kept in a bright, sunny spot. During the season of active growth they benefit by liberal applications of water, but after the magnificent flowers have faded a rest-period of 2 to 3 weeks' duration should be given them. (I,H)

Scaphyglottis violacea

F. C. HOEHNE

S. Hadweni (*had*-wen-eye) (Brazil; Guianas)

Pbs. pendulous, clustered, to about 2½" long, cylindrical, prominently jointed. Lvs. sharply pendulous, solitary on the pbs., rather soft-textured, dark green, to almost 2' long, whiplike. Infls. borne from pb.-bases or on special leafless pb.-like growths, 1½–8" long, pendulous or arching. Fls. solitary, waxy, fragrant, long-lasting, to 3" across, the ss. and ps. yellow with large blotches of bright brown, the somewhat tubular lip white or cream-white, irregularly spotted with bright red, the col.-face flushed with red. Spring–fall. (I,H)

S. Steelii (*steel*-ee-eye)   (Brazil; Guianas; Venezuela)

Rather similar in habit to *S. Hadweni*, but the lvs. to more than 4′ long. Infls. 1–3-fld., pendulous. Fls. fragrant, waxy, long-lasting, to more than 3″ across, the ss. and ps. yellow irregularly blotched (mostly in transverse zones) with reddish brown, the somewhat flaring tubular lip pale yellow irregularly blotched with red, especially on the sides. Fall. (I,H)

Scuticaria Steelii

VEITCH

SOBRALIA
(sow-*bral*-ee-ah)

Upwards of 35 species of *Sobralia* are recognized in the region extending from Mexico to Peru and Brazil. Variously epiphytic, lithophytic, or terrestrial in habit, they are odd reedlike plants, often of huge dimensions. Their incredibly beautiful and complex flowers resemble certain Cattleyas in form, and even rival those orchids in magnificence. Unfortunately, these blossoms usually last but a single day, though they are produced successively over long periods of time. Sobralias are as yet scarce in our collections, but they are superb orchids which deserve more attention.

CULTURE: Although in nature some of them are epiphytes, in the collection all Sobralias should be treated as semiterrestrials and grown in large, well-drained pots in a compost such as that recommended for *Cymbidium*. While actively growing they need quantities of water, but when the new leafy stems have reached their full development, moisture should be lessened for a month or so to afford them a rest-period. During the major growth period, they benefit by liberal applications of manure-water or other fertilizing materials. Exposure to rather bright light ensures proper flower production. One of the most important points to remember, when dealing with Sobralias, is not to disturb them any more than is absolutely necessary; even repotting will in many cases cause them not to flower for several years. Most of these majestic orchids occur in tropical areas, hence they require warm or intermediate temperatures. (I,H)

S. decora (de-*koe*-rah)   (Mexico to Costa Rica)

Sts. clustered, 12–30" tall, with the lower surfaces of the lvs. and their sheaths black-warty or -fuzzy. Lvs. 2–9" long, folded. Infls. very short, 1–2-fld. Fls. fragrant, about 3–4" across, the ss. and ps. usually white or blush-white, the large tubular lip rose-purple or lavender streaked with yellow and brown on the disc. Spring–summer. (I,H)

S. macrantha (mak-*ran*-thah)   (Mexico to Costa Rica)

Sts. tightly clustered, 2–8' tall and more. Lvs. rigid, folded, 5–12" long. Infls. several-fld., the fls. produced singly over a long period. Fls.

Sobralia leucoxantha

rather fleshy, short-lived, fragrant, highly variable in size and color, 6–10" across, usually rose-purple (a pure white form is known), with the large, ornate, widely flared, tubular lip white on the side of basal part, tinged centrally with yellow, the marginal area usually darker purple than other segms. Spring–fall. (I,H)

SOPHRONITIS
(sof-row-*nye*-tiss)

Six species of *Sophronitis* are known, all of them smallish or very dwarf epiphytic or lithophytic orchids, endemic to Brazil. One of them is occasionally encountered in choice contemporary collections, where its incredibly vivid scarlet flowers have found favor with hybridists, who use them to impart rich hues to crosses with the allied Cattleyas and other groups.

CULTURE: Generally as for *Cattleya*, although a shaded spot is requisite and the plants must never be allowed to become dry. (I)

S. coccinea (kok-*sin*-ee-ah)   (Brazil)

Often known by its synonym, *S. grandiflora*. Pbs. spindle-shaped to ovoid, 1–1½" long. Lf. solitary, rigidly leathery, dark glossy-green,

Sophronitis coccinea

ROD MC LELLAN COMPANY

2½–3" long. Infls. short, usually 1-fld. Fls. highly variable in size and coloration, 1½–3" in diam., usually glittering scarlet, with the base and lat. lbs. of the lip orange-yellow streaked with scarlet. Forms with rich carmine-purple or bright rose-purple fls. are known. Fall–winter. (I,H)

SPATHOGLOTTIS
(spath-oh-*glaw*-tiss)

Spathoglottis contains about 40 species of largely handsome terrestrial (sometimes lithophytic) orchids widespread from southern China and the Himalayas throughout Malaysia and Indonesia to the Philippines,

New Caledonia, and Samoa. It is allied to *Calanthe* and *Phaius*, but the plants bear different-shaped, often lovely, medium-sized to large blossoms in tall erect racemes. Spathoglottis is not as yet widely grown by orchidists, but the group offers much of interest to the collector.

CULTURE: As for *Phaius*. In sufficiently warm climates these orchids do well when planted in special outdoor beds, such as are suggested for *Arachnis*. (I,H)

S. aurea (*aw*-ree-ah)   (Malay Peninsula; Indonesia)

Pbs. small, rather irregular. Lvs. narrow, folded, to 2′ long and 1½″ broad, stalked, often purple-tinged. Infls. to more than 2′ tall, loosely 4–10-fld., the fls. opening successively. Fls. to 2¾″ across, rich dark golden yellow, the lat. lbs. of the lip more or less flushed or spotted with crimson, the calli and base of midlb. with small crimson spots arranged in rows. Spring. (I,H)

S. plicata (ply-*kah*-tah)   (Tropical Asia and Indonesia)

Pbs. tightly clustered, ovoid to rather conical, often irregular, to 1½″ tall, bright or dull green. Lvs. sheathing basally, narrow, folded, to more than 2′ long, 2–3″ broad. Infls. rather rigidly erect, to 2½′ tall, the rac. densely 5–25-fld., with large, often pinkish bracts, the fls. opening successively over a long period. Fls. often self-pollinating, extremely variable in size, to a maximum of about 1½″ across, the ss. and ps. violet-red or pinkish-purple, the lip with bright yellow basal calli, sometimes median-spotted with magenta. Throughout the year, often almost everblooming. (I,H)

STANHOPEA
(stan-*hoe*-pee-ah)

About 25 species make up the genus *Stanhopea*, which contains some of the most remarkably formed of all orchidaceous plants. These are variously epiphytic or lithophytic over the area from Mexico to Peru and Brazil, and certain of them are relatively frequent in our collections today, almost invariably under incorrect names. The flower-spikes arise from the base of the pseudobulb and hang sharply downward; each spike produces one to a few often huge and typically very intricate, waxy, short-lived, headily fragrant blossoms, whose shape gives them, in the American tropics, the common name of "El Toro," which means "The Bull." Often the inflated buds open with an audible snapping sound.

CULTURE: The basic cultural requirements of Stanhopeas are readily

Spathoglottis plicata

G. C. K. DUNSTERVILLE

met, even by the novice, hence these fantastic orchids are heartily recommended to all enthusiasts who delight in the unusual. Because of the strictly pendulous nature of the inflorescences, the plants must be grown in baskets, or on slabs or rafts; if kept in pots, the flower-spikes still grow downward, and may even attempt to open deep within the compost! A perfectly drained potting-medium is requisite, with straight, tight-packed osmunda fiber being generally used. Stanhopeas should be kept well shaded at all times, furnished with copious water and high humidity, and never allowed to dry out completely. While in especially active growth, frequent applications of fertilizer prove beneficial. Warm or intermediate temperatures are needed by all members of this genus currently cultivated. (I,H)

S. graveolens (gra-*vee*-oh-lenz)   (Mexico to Brazil)

Pbs. ovoid to almost conical, 1–1½" long, clustered, becoming grooved and wrinkled with age. Lf. solitary, firm, folded, to 2' long, stalked basally. Infls. short, pendulous, 1–6-fld., the rachis enveloped in several papery, spathelike bracts. Fls. very fragrant, waxy, to 5″ long, variable in color and somewhat so in structural details, varying from white to pale yellow or yellow with reddish brown or purple dots, the ss. and ps. often with more or less circular rings of dark color, the base of the amazingly complicated lip with or without 2 lateral dark purple eyes or blotches. Spring–early summer. (I,H)

S. Wardii (*ward*-ee-eye)   (Mexico to Panama)

Pbs. clustered, ovoid-conical, grooved, somewhat angled, to 3″ long. Lf. rigidly leathery, folded, to 1½′ long and 6½″ broad, with a slender stalk. Infls. usually 3–9-fld., the fls. rather crowded. Fls. very fragrant, to 5″ across, the ss. and ps. pale yellow, cream-white, or greenish white blotched or dotted with brownish purple or reddish purple, the basal part of the complex lip orange-yellow or maroon with a large purple-brown spot on each side, the apical parts pale yellow. Mostly fall. (I,H)

STELIS
(*stel*-iss)

This is a remarkable genus of probably more than 500 species of mostly very small and rarely cultivated epiphytic or lithophytic orchids. They

Stanhopea Wardii

H. A. DUNN

are widely distributed from Cuba and Mexico to Brazil and Peru, with a particularly rich representation in the high mountains of Central and northern South America. *Stelis* is somewhat allied to *Masdevallia* and *Pleurothallis*, differing in its mostly triangular flowers which but rarely measure more than ¼″ in diameter. Of interest to connoisseurs of the "botanical" orchids, these fascinating little plants should form a part of even the most modest collection.

CULTURE: As for *Pleurothallis*, depending upon the place of origin of the particular species or individual under consideration. (C,I,H)

S. ciliaris (sil-ee-*ah*-riss)   (Mexico to Costa Rica)

Sts. clustered, stout, to 1¼″ long, sheathed. Lf. solitary, narrow, fleshy, erect, 1¼–6″ long, to 1¼″ broad. Infls. erect, loosely many-fld., slender, exceeding the lvs., with obliquely tubular reddish floral bracts. Fls. to about ⅜″ in diam., often lasting rather well, extremely variable in shape, ranging from dark maroon to purplish, the ss. usually with long hairs mostly on the margins, the ps., lip and col. very small and intricate, hidden at center of the ss. Mostly spring. (I)

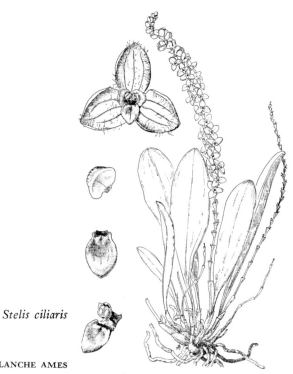

Stelis ciliaris

DRAWING BY BLANCHE AMES

THUNIA
(*thoo*-nee-ah)

About 8 species of *Thunia* are recognized, all of them majestic terrestrial or semiepiphytic orchids native to the mountainous areas of
India and Burma. The genus is allied to *Phaius*, but has tall, canelike
stems furnished with quickly deciduous foliage, and apical clusters of
large, showy flowers shaped much like Cattleyas. Unfortunately,
Thunias are rare in contemporary collections, though they are splendid
plants, of easy cultural requirements.

CULTURE: These orchids should be grown in pots, in a perfectly
drained compost such as is recommended for *Phaius*. While actively
growing, they should be kept in a sunny spot, and given quantities of
moisture, high humidity, and fertilizer. As soon as the flowers have
faded and the foliage starts to yellow and fall, lower temperatures
should be provided, coupled with an almost complete stoppage of
water. Annual repotting and division of the cane-clumps may be attended to shortly thereafter. The bare canes in this genus may be cut
up into lengths of about 6″ each, and propagated in moist sand or
sphagnum moss; new plantlets will sprout from most of the nodes.
Thunias are susceptible to the attacks of thrips and red spider, and
these pests should be watched for at all times when foliage is present
on the plants. (I)

T. Marshalliana (mar-shal-ee-*ah*-nah)   (Burma)

Pbs. canelike, to more than 3′ tall, leafy throughout. Lvs. pale green
above, rather powdery beneath, soon deciduous. Infls. apical, drooping,
3–12-fld., with large white bracts. Fls. fragrant, long-lasting, to 5″
across, the spreading ss. and ps. pure glittering white, the large tubular-
flaring lip white, its midlb. crisped marginally, golden-yellow, with
numerous forked dark orange-red veins, the tubular part usually
streaked with yellow and purple, the disc with 5 yellow raised keels
and 5 shorter ones on each side, all fringed with crystalline hairs. June–
Aug. (I)

TRICHOCENTRUM
(try-koe-*sen*-trum)

Trichocentrum consists of about 18 species of mostly very dwarf
epiphytic (rarely lithophytic) orchids, ranging from Mexico to southern Brazil. These are unusual little plants—only gradually becoming
known by specialist hobbyists—with profuse, proportionately large,

handsome, long-lasting flowers. Easily grown and flowering over periods of several months, they are highly recommended to all orchidists.

CULTURE: As for *Ornithocephalus*. (I,H)

T. albo-coccineum (*al*-bow-kok-*sin*-ee-um)   (Ecuador; Peru; Brazil)

Usually grown under its synonym, *T. albo-purpureum*. Pbs. almost absent. Lf. solitary (rarely paired), rigidly leathery, sometimes reddish-spotted or flushed beneath with purplish, narrowed basally, to about 4" long and 1½" broad. Infls. basal, usually creeping and horizontal, bearing 1–5 or more fls. in succession over a period of several months. Fls. about 2" long, usually opening flat, long-lived, heavy-textured, variable in color, the spreading ss. and ps. usually greenish yellow outside, inside brownish yellow or olive-brown, the proportionately huge lip white with a pale or vivid dark purplish or reddish purple blotch and bright yellow disc-keels. Mostly late summer–fall. (I,H)

TRICHOGLOTTIS
(try-koe-*glaw*-tiss)

This is a genus of about 35 species of principally epiphytic, vinelike orchids, somewhat related to *Vanda*, which are widespread in the Asiatic and Indonesian tropics. Very diverse in vegetative structure, most of the commonly cultivated species somewhat resemble a small *Renanthera* in structure. The flowers of many species are rather large and are produced in small or large numbers on abbreviated inflorescences from the nodes of the leafy stem. These blossoms, mostly of heavy texture, are generally fragrant, long-lasting, and variable in color, being often barred or blotched with a darker color on a pale ground. Most species of *Trichoglottis* are as yet very scarce in our collections.

CULTURE: As for *Arachnis* and *Renanthera*. (I,H)

T. brachiata (brak-ee-*ah*-tah)   (Philippines)

Basically resembling *T. philippinensis* (of which it is sometimes considered a variant). The numerous heavy lvs. are more rigid and ascending, very densely cloaking the climbing st. Fls. produced abundantly, heavily fragrant, lasting for more than a month, about 2" in diameter, the ss. and ps. often almost black-purple with a narrow cream-white or white margin, the complex fuzzy lip mostly magenta. Summer. (I,H)

T. fasciata (fass-ee-*ah*-tah)   (Philippines and Thailand to Sumatra)

Sts. relatively thick, climbing, to 5′ long, the lvs. heavily leathery, bilobed at tips, to 6″ long and 2″ broad. Fls. 2–4 on an infl. about 6″ long, more than 2″ across, waxy, long-lasting, fragrant. Ss. and ps. whitish on reverse side, pale lemon-yellow on front with brown cross-bars of irregular formation. Lip fuzzy, white with a few brown spots and marks. Mostly spring–early summer. (I,H)

Trichoglottis brachiata

REG S. DAVIS

T. philippinensis (fil-i-pin-*en*-siss)   (Philippines)

Sts. relatively thick, usually erect, angled, to 5′ tall in very old specimens, rather densely covered with short, glossy, recurving lvs. several inches in length. Fls. solitary or paired, fragrant, long-lasting, on very short stalks at the stem-nodes, waxy, the ss. and ps. mostly reddish tan with more or less broad cream-white margins, the complex fuzzy lip mostly cream-white. Summer. (I,H)

TRICHOPILIA
(try-koe-*pil*-ee-ah)

Trichopilia is a genus of about 30 species of epiphytic, lithophytic, or rarely terrestrial orchids, a few of which are sometimes seen in particularly comprehensive collections. They range from Mexico and Cuba to Brazil, and produce a profusion of generally large, ornate, *Cattleya*-like flowers from odd, pseudobulbous, clump-forming plants.

CULTURE: As for *Oncidium*. (I,H)

T. marginata (mar-ji-*nah*-tah)   (Guatemala to Colombia)

Pbs. strongly compressed, clustered, narrow, 2¼–5½" long, the bases enveloped in several papery, usually blotched sheaths. Lf. solitary, leathery, dark dull green, 4½–12" long. Infls. basal, short, 2–3-fld., arching to pendulous. Fls. rather fragrant, heavy-textured, to 4" across, highly variable in color, usually with the ss. and ps. reddish with paler margins, the tubular lip usually white outside, the inner tube dark rose-red, the reflexed, wavy margins of midlb. often white. Spring. (I,H)

T. suavis (*swa*-viss)   (Costa Rica; Panama; Colombia)

Pbs. rather fleshy, crowded, somewhat compressed laterally, usually almost round, mostly dull grayish green, to 3" long. Lf. solitary, rather

H. A. DUNN

Trichopilia suavis

leathery, 4–14" long, to 3" broad, narrowed below into a short stalk. Infls. short, 2–5-fld., arching or pendulous. Fls. very fragrant, to 4" across, variable in color, the ss. and ps. white or cream-white, sometimes sparsely spotted with pale rose-pink or red, the very large, ornate lip white or cream-white usually heavily spotted with rose-pink, the throat mostly marked with yellow or orange, very rarely red-blotched, the margins of flaring midlb. handsomely crisped and toothed. Mostly Mar.–Apr. (I)

TRIGONIDIUM
(trig-oh-*nid*-ee-um)

About a dozen species make up the genus *Trigonidium*, only one of which appears to be at all frequent in cultivation. These unusual and rather attractive epiphytic orchids range from Mexico to Brazil. The group is somewhat allied to *Maxillaria*, but the structure of its solitary, rather urn-shaped flowers—borne at the tops of tall, bracted scapes—is very different.

CULTURE: As for the tropical Maxillarias or Oncidiums. (I,H)

T. Egertonianum (ej-er-tow-nee-*ah*-num)   (Mexico to Colombia)

Pbs. clustered, egg-shaped, ridged, usually compressed laterally, glossy yellowish in most specimens, to 3″ tall. Lvs. 2, long-stalked below, glossy, rather leathery, narrow, to 2′ long and 1¼″ wide. Infls. often several at once, erect, to 1½′ tall, enveloped in tubular, papery bracts. Fls. about 1½″ long, lasting well, the ss. varying from greenish yellow to pinkish tan, with or without brown or purple stripes, the smaller ps. similar in color but with a brown, purple, or iridescent blue glandular apical thickening, the lip usually yellowish tan with brown or red stripes. Mostly spring. (I,H)

VANDA
(*van*-dah)

More than 70 species of *Vanda* are known, and—together with the thousands of magnificent hybrids made both within this genus and with allied groups—these form a most important part of every present-day orchid collection. They are grown commercially on an impressive scale, especially in such warm areas as Hawaii, Malaya, and southern Florida. Mostly epiphytic in habit (some few of them are predominantly lithophytic or terrestrial in the wild), they occur over a broad region extending from China and the Himalayas throughout Southeast Asia and Indonesia to New Guinea and northern Australia. The Vandas are highly diverse in vegetative and floral appearance, but almost all of them are well worthy of cultivation, because of the generally large dimensions of the abundant, long-lasting blossoms.

CULTURE: Most Vandas are easily grown and brought into flower, hence they are highly recommended to the hobbyist. Pot- or basket-culture is usually adopted, with perfectly drained composts varying from straight tight-packed osmunda to several different mixtures composed of tree-fern fiber, bark preparation, and even chunks of volcanic pumice. Like most orchids of this alliance, they grow throughout the year, hence must never be allowed to dry out. Sun-lovers (most of the species and hybrids with terete or semiterete leaves will not flower without full sun-exposure), they delight in heavy watering, high humidity, and liberal fertilizing at all times. Temperatures for the majority of these plants should be warm, or at least intermediate. (I,H)

V. coerulea (see-*roo*-lee-ah) (Himalayas to Burma)

St. robust, to 4' tall in very old specimens, very densely leafy. Lvs. rigidly leathery, to 10" long and about 1" wide, irregularly cut and toothed at apex. Infls. mostly erect or gracefully arching, to 2' tall, mostly 5–15-fld. Fls. highly variable in shape, color, and size, to 4" across at most, the ss. and ps. typically pale blue with darker reticulations (varying to pure white and pink in certain very rare forms), the small lip mostly very dark purple-blue. Mostly fall–winter. (I)

V. teres (*ter*-eez) (Himalayan foothills to Burma and Thailand)

St. terete, often profusely branching both from near base and above, forming dense tangled masses many feet long. Lvs. similar to the st., 4–8" long, erect or rather sharply ascending. Infls. 6–12" long, borne opposite the lf.-bases from upper parts of st., 3–6-fld., rather loose. Fls. 3–4" in diam., rather long-lasting, variable in color, fragrant. Ss. and ps. pale rose-purple more or less suffused with white, the complex, fishtail-shaped lip tawny yellow, red, and pale rose-purple. Almost everblooming in the tropics, otherwise usually May–July. (H)

V. tricolor (*try*-kol-or) (Java; Bali)

St. robust, rooting freely, to several feet tall in old specimens, leafy throughout. Lvs. gracefully curving, heavy-textured, to 18" long and 1½" broad. Infls. with rather stout stalks, usually shorter than the lvs., 7–12-fld. Fls. 2–3" long, waxy and long-lasting, very fragrant, variable in shape and very much so in coloration, in the typical phase the ss. and ps. similar, sharply narrowed basally, the ps. often twisted almost completely around, light yellow more or less densely spotted with bright (or dull) reddish brown, the spots arranged in longitudinal rows and often confluent, sometimes covering the greater part of the surface, outside white. Lip 3-lbd., rather large, the lat. lbs. white, the midlb. complex, whitish at base with some red-brown streaks, the remaining part bright or dull magenta-purple. Fall–winter. (I,H)

—var. **suavis** (*swa*-viss) (Java)

Usually grown under its synonym, *V. suavis*. Differs from the typical form in its mostly longer infls., more numerous and exceedingly sweet-scented fls., the ground color of ss. and ps. white, the less numerous spots vivid red-purple or magenta-purple, the basal half of lip dark magenta-purple, the apical half paler. Fall–winter. (I,H)

H. A. DUNN   GEORGE FULLER

Vanda teres

Vanda tricolor var. *suavis*
(upper raceme) and
Vanda tricolor (lower raceme)

VANDOPSIS
(van-*dop*-siss)

Vandopsis is a genus of about 12 species of typically robust and spectacular epiphytic or lithophytic orchids, allied to *Renanthera* and *Arachnis*, which inhabit the region extending from China through the Ryukyu Islands to New Guinea. As yet scarce in our collections, they are all large plants bearing racemes of heavy-textured flowers which often persist in good condition for several months.

CULTURE: The cultivated kinds of Vandopsis should be grown much in the manner recommended for the tropical Vandas. Most of them require full exposure to the sun to flower properly. Heavy fertilizing is obligatory. (I,H)

V. gigantea (jy-*gan*-tee-ah)   (Burma)

Sts. usually short, stout, seldom to 1′ tall. Lvs. few, tongue-shaped, to 2′ long and 2½″ broad, extremely heavy and rigidly leathery. Infls. pendulous or strongly arching, loosely 6–18-fld., to 1′ long. Fls. to about 3″ across, often lasting for several months, vaguely fragrant at times, very thick and heavy-textured, the ss. and ps. yellow with concentric rings of light brown, the lip yellow, with a high white keel down the middle. Mostly spring–summer. (I,H)

V. lissochiloides (liss-ok-i-*loy*-deez)   (Philippines; Moluccas)

St. very robust, to more than 6′ tall, leafy throughout. Lvs. arranged horizontally, very heavy and rigidly leathery, to 2′ long and 2″ broad.

Vandopsis lissochiloides

REG S. DAVIS

Infls. robust, rigidly erect, to 8′ tall, loosely 12–30-fld., the fls. opening successively over a period of many months. Fls. very heavy-textured, extremely long-lived, sweetly fragrant, to about 3″ long, rather variable in color, the typical phase with the outside of the ss. and ps. densely spotted with rich magenta (sometimes wholly magenta), the inside yellow, blotched with magenta-purple, the complex lip yellow and magenta-red. Mostly summer, but in the tropics almost everblooming. (H)

VANILLA
(vah-*nil*-ah)

Vanilla, according to most recent estimates, contains 110 species of odd vinelike orchids. These are, in the wild, variously terrestrial, lithophytic, or truly epiphytic, and either bear large fleshy leaves or are essentially leafless. They occur in almost all of the tropical and subtropical parts of the earth, though they reach their most impressive development in Brazil, Tropical Africa, and the West Indies. The flowers of *Vanilla* are for the most part large, intricate in structure, and spectacular. While, unfortunately, they often last only a day or two, the flowering season may extend over a period of many months. Several members of this genus are economically important, producing from their seed-capsules the substance from which commercial vanilla extract is prepared. The cultivation of these Vanillas has been an important industry, notably in Mexico, Malagasy (Madagascar), and Tahiti, but their product is now being largely supplanted by synthetic vanilla. As yet, these attractive viny plants are little known by orchidists.

CULTURE: When mature, most of the Vanillas are very lengthy vines. They must, therefore, be given some sort of support in the greenhouse, such as a trellis. The base of the plant may be placed in a well-drained pot, filled with a compost such as that suggested in this volume for *Phaius*, with the viny stems trained upward. Most of the members of this diverse genus will not flower until the plants are quite large, and until they are exposed to very bright light. Growing throughout the year, they need to be kept moist and in a humid situation at all times, and they seem to benefit by liberal and frequent applications of fertilizing solution. (I,H)

V. planifolia (plan-i-*foe*-lee-ah)   (Tropical America)

Sts. elongate, often many feet in length, sparsely or profusely branching, slender or stout, leafy, rooting at most nodes. Lvs. somewhat succulent, glossy rich green, in robust forms to 9″ long and 3″ broad. Infls. axillary, to about 3″ long, the 20 or so fls. produced usually singly but in succession. Fls. not opening fully, fragrant, fleshy but short-lived, about 2½" long, greenish yellow, the complex tubular lip often whitish on the disc, the central part irregularly fringed. Throughout the year, often almost everblooming in well established specimens. (I,H)

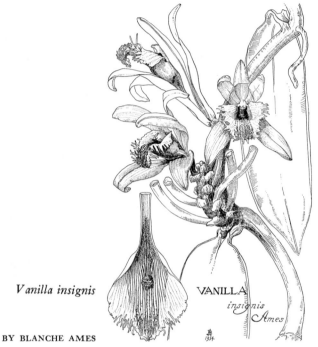

Vanilla insignis

VANILLA
insignis
Ames

DRAWING BY BLANCHE AMES

XYLOBIUM
(zi-*low*-bee-um)

Some 20 or more species of primarily epiphytic orchids make up this interesting genus, which is allied to *Lycaste*, though the individual flowers—borne in often large dense racemes—resemble those of *Maxillaria* in shape. Prominent fleshy pseudobulbs give rise to one or more large folded leaves, and the basal flower-spikes are often produced in considerable numbers on large specimens. Though not particularly showy, the blossoms have a charming fragrance and are sufficiently attractive to warrant further attention by enthusiasts.

CULTURE: Since most of the Xylobiums in our collections are lowland species, their cultural requirements approximate those afforded the warm-growing Lycastes. (I,H)

X. elongatum (ee-lon-*gah*-tum)   (Central America)

Pbs. elongate, cylindric, to 8″ tall, topped by two leathery, somewhat folded, glossy green lvs. to 1′ long. Infls. erect, to 7″ tall, with up to 20 fls. about 1½″ across, not opening fully. Fls. fragrant, rather long-lasting, bright or pale yellow. Lip variable, usually dark brown-purple. Late spring–summer. (I)

X. foveatum (foe-vee-*ah*-tum)   (Mexico and Jamaica to Peru)

Variable species, both in vegetative size and fl. shape. Pbs. stout, vaguely egg-shaped, furrowed with age, to 4″ long. Lvs. 2 or 3, leathery, folded, to 1½′ long. Infls. erect, to 1′ tall, crowded with numerous fragrant fls. about 1″ across. Ss. and ps. cream-white or yellowish. Lip cream-white with some red median veins. Fall–winter. (I,H)

X. squalens (s*kwah*-lenz)   (Venezuela)

Pbs. clustered, egg-shaped, to 3″ tall. Lvs. paired, leathery, somewhat folded, to 1½′ long. Infls. to 6″ tall, rather densely 15–20-fld., the fls.

Xylobium chapadense

F. C. HOEHNE

about 1¼″ long, vaguely fragrant, rather waxy. Ss. and ps. yellowish or cream-white, often flushed with rose-red, the ps. sometimes purple-streaked. Lip whitish or yellowish, the side lbs. dark purple, the midlb. generally streaked with purple. Mostly summer–late fall. (I,H)

ZYGOPETALUM
(zye-goe-*peh*-tah-lum)

The orchid genus *Zygopetalum* contains about 25 species of handsome terrestrial, lithophytic, or epiphytic plants ranging from Venezuela and the Guianas to Brazil, where most of them occur. These plants produce extremely lovely and fragrant, vividly colored blossoms in erect spikes from the base of the medium-sized pseudobulbs. The flowers, often in shades of brilliant green, blue, or purple, are excellently suited for corsages or as cut material, and for this reason one of the species, *Z. intermedium*, is rather widely grown by commercial establishments. A few hybrid forms have been made within *Zygopetalum*, and it has been successfully crossed as well with *Colax* and *Lycaste*, to give *Zygocolax* and *Zygocaste*.

CULTURE: Most of the Zygopetalums in contemporary collections are best treated as terrestrials, being grown in well-drained pots of rich humus and oak leaf-mould, well supplied with leached manure. They delight in a fresh and airy situation, and at all times require abundant sunshine—but not so brilliant that the foliage burns and becomes unsightly. A definite rest of about 3 weeks' duration should be given them upon completion of the new growths, and watering commenced only when the eyes again start to sprout. (C,I)

Z. intermedium (in-ter-*mee*-dee-um) (Brazil)

This orchid is generally grown under the name of *Zygopetalum Mackayi*, which applies to a completely distinct and much rarer orchid. Pbs. pale green, glossy, to 4″ tall, rather egg-shaped, with some leafy bracts at the base and a few long (to 3′) rather soft narrow lvs. at the top. Infls. erect, to 2′ tall, with up to 12 handsome fls. to 3″ across, lasting for several weeks in perfection and giving off a delicious and heady fragrance. Ss. and ps. spreading, green or yellowish green with blotches and bars of purple-brown, the large lip white, intricately marked with lines and dots of blue or purple-blue, the margin crisped. The fuzzy lip-surface immediately distinguishes this species from the allied Z. *Mackayi*, which is completely smooth on the lip. Fall–winter. (C,I)

Z. Mackayi (mah-*kay*-eye) (Brazil)

An extremely rare orchid in cultivation today, this name typically being applied to the allied Z. *intermedium*. *Zygopetalum Mackayi* resembles the other species in almost all ways, but has smaller fls. with a completely hairless lip. Flowers are produced mostly during the winter months. (C,I)

Zygopetalum Mackayi

Flora Brasílica

IV

Hybrids and Hybridization

PRODUCTION AND NAMING OF HYBRIDS

The orchid family is unique among all groups of flowering plants in the tremendous number of classified hybrids that have been made from its members. No other plant family can boast of artificially (and also naturally) produced hybrid forms that outnumber the original species. The total of approximately 25,000 registered hybrids, as against a probable 24,000 species of orchids, is being increased at the rate of about 1,000 a year.

The official registrars are the Royal Horticultural Society, London, England, though formerly this post was held by the commercial firm of Sanders (St. Albans) Ltd. Each issue of the British publication, *The Orchid Review*, in which all new hybrids are registered before their incorporation in the official *Hybrid Lists*, contains almost a hundred additional hybrid names, with their corresponding parentages.

Historical Note

Because of this extraordinary breeding activity, more than casual attention should be paid to the subject of hybridization. Its history dates from the year 1856, when the first artificially produced cross between two orchid species was brought into flower in England. This plant, hybridized in 1852 and named *Calanthe x Dominyi* by the British orchidologist Rolfe in honor of its originator, J. Dominy, foreman and principal grower of orchidaceous plants at the establishment of Messrs. Veitch & Sons, Chelsea, was the product of the fertilization of the Indian *Calanthe masuca* by *Calanthe furcata*, from the same country. Though now uncommon in cultivation, it is a handsome plant.

Some years later, in 1863, Dominy, having created several additional hybrids, succeeded in bringing the first bigeneric orchid cross (a hybrid between members of two distinct generic groups) into flower; this was *Laeliocattleya x Exoniensis*, a cross between *Cattleya Mossiae* (which correctly is *C. labiata* var. *Mossiae*) and *Laelia crispa*.

For many years, Dominy was virtually the only person doing experimental work with the hybridization of orchids, though by the year 1890 some two hundred different hybrid forms were on record. Today hybrid orchids are particularly numerous among the various genera cultivated for commercial purposes, such as the several components of the *Cattleya* group, *Cymbidium*, *Odontoglossum* (and its several allied

Dendrobium x Helen Fukumura

T. FUKUMURA

aggregations,—*Miltonia*, *Cochlioda*, and *Oncidium*), *Dendrobium*, *Paphiopedilum*, and the sarcanthads (monopodials), *Phalaenopsis* and *Vanda*, for example.

Multigeneric Crosses

In contemporary breeding tremendous complexity of hybrids is attained, with the result that we have many bigeneric crosses (utilizing two distinct genera), trigeneric (three genera), and even quadrigeneric (four genera) ones. A primary hybrid is one in which two species are utilized to form an artificially (or sometimes, naturally) induced hybrid plant; these primaries are usually rather intermediate in form and coloration between the male (staminate) and female (pistillate) parents, and the progeny usually exhibits proportionately little variation. Examples of this type of hybrid are found in such well-known crosses as *Epidendrum x O'Brienianum* (*E. evectum* $\times$ *E. ibaguense*), and *Cymbidium x Langleyense* (*C. Devonianum* $\times$ *C. Lowianum*).

If, however, a hybrid be further crossed with a second hybrid, genetic complexities arise within the progeny, with the result that varying extremes in coloration and, to a degree, form, may be anticipated. A further characteristic of such hybrids is that dominant genetic characters of one or more of the involved parents may be evident in the offspring, often with unexpected results. In certain hybrids a species in the genealogical background may be so dominant that all or at least a part of the progeny are exact duplicates of that parent; a fine example of this is the handsome Brazilian orchid *Zygopetalum intermedium* (generally grown under the erroneous name of *Z. Mackayi*, which applies to an entirely different species), which when crossed, for example, with a species of *Cattleya* or *Dendrobium*—with which *Zygopetalum* has scant affinity—produces viable seed and seedlings that all grow into plants like the parent *Zygopetalum*, with no alteration whatsoever of form or coloration, either of the vegetative or floral parts. If, however, this same plant be hybridized with an allied genus, such as *Colax* or *Lycaste*, the progeny are found to be distinctive bigeneric hybrids, to which the names *Zygocolax* and *Zygocaste*, respectively, are given. The "false" *Zygopetalum* hybrids are the result of parthenogenesis, a complex condition whereby the ovules are stimulated into the production of viable seeds, but are not actually fertilized by the sperm cells from the pollen-tubes of the secondary "parent."

Bigeneric hybrids, crosses between members of two distinct genera or groups, as well as the much more complex trigenerics and quadrigenerics, naturally exhibit a great deal of variability, both as to vegetative and floral form and floral coloration. The following is a list of these multigeneric hybrid groups, as recorded to date,[1] with the genera utilized in the production of each. The asterisks following the generic parentage indicate whether they are bigeneric (**), trigeneric (***), or quadrigeneric (****).

[1] It is, of course, almost impossible to assure the reader that this list is complete by the time this volume reaches his hands, since scarcely a month passes without one or more new multigeneric hybrid groups being officially registered.

Adaglossum (Ada × Odontoglossum)**
Adioda (Ada × Cochlioda)**
Aeridachnis (Aerides × Arachnis)**

Vanda x Maurice Restrepo

Aeridopsis (Aerides × Phalaenopsis)**
Aeridostylis (Aerides × Rhynchostylis)**
Aeridovanda (Aerides × Vanda)**
Angulocaste (Anguloa × Lycaste)**

Anoectomaria (Anoectochilus × Haemaria)**

Arachnopsis (Arachnis × Phalaenopsis)**

Aranda (Arachnis × Vanda)**

Aranthera (Arachnis × Renanthera)**

Armodachnis (Armodorum × Arachnis)**

Ascocenda (Ascocentrum × Vanda)**

Aspasium (Aspasia × Oncidium)**

Brapasia (Brassia × Aspasia)**

Brassidium (Brassia × Oncidium)**

Brassocattleya (Brassavola × Cattleya)**[1]

Brassodiacrium (Brassavola × Diacrium)**[1,2]

Brassoepidendrum (Brassavola × Epidendrum)**[1]

Brassolaelia (Brassavola × Laelia)**[1]

Brassolaeliocattleya (Brassavola × Laelia × Cattleya)***[1]

Brassophronitis (Brassavola × Sophronitis)**[1]

Brassotonia (Brassavola × Broughtonia)**

Burrageara (Cochlioda × Miltonia × Odontoglossum × Oncidium)****

Cattleytonia (Broughtonia × Cattleya)**

Charleswortheara (Cochlioda × Miltonia × Oncidium)***

Chondrobollea (Chondrorhyncha × Bollea)**

Chondropetalum (Chondrorhyncha × Zygopetalum)**

Colmanara (Miltonia × Odontoglossum × Oncidium)***

Cycnodes (Cycnoches × Mormodes)**

Dekensara (Schomburgkia × Brassavola × Cattleya)***[1,3]

Diabroughtonia (Diacrium × Broughtonia)**[2]

Diacattleya (Diacrium × Cattleya)**[2]

Dialaelia (Diacrium × Laelia)**[2]

Dialaeliocattleya (Diacrium × Laelia × Cattleya)***[2]

Dossinimaria (Dossinia × Haemaria)**

Epicattleya (Epidendrum × Cattleya)**

Epidiacrium (Epidendrum × Diacrium)**[2]

[1] For the sake of convenience, these confused multigeneric groups are recognized as valid, even though most of them contain hybrids in which the orchids correctly known as *Rhyncholaelia Digbyana* and *R. glauca* (usually called Brassavolas in horticulture) figure prominently; a few true Brassavolas have also been used in certain of these groups.

[2] *Diacrium* is now botanically referred to *Caularthron*, but no benefit seems evident by altering the epithets of these already fully established hybrid aggregations.

[3] For the sake of convenience, and to avoid further confusion, these multigeneric groups are here recognized as valid, despite the contemporary reduction of *Schomburgkia* to sectional status under *Laelia*.

Epigoa (Epidendrum × Domingoa)**
Epilaelia (Epidendrum × Laelia)**
Epiliaeliocattleya (Epidendrum × Laelia × Cattleya)***
Epilaeliopsis (Epidendrum × Laeliopsis)**
Epiphronitella (Epidendrum × Sophronitella)**
Epiphronitis (Epidendrum × Sophronitis)**
Gastocalanthe (Gastorchis × Calanthe)**
Gastophaius (Gastorchis × Phaius)**
Grammatocymbidium (Grammatophyllum × Cymbidium)**
Hawaiiara (Vanda × Renanthera × Vandopsis)***
Holttumara (Arachnis × Vanda × Renanthera)***
Iwanagara (Diacrium × Brassavola × Laelia × Cattleya)****[1,2]
Laeliocattleya (Laelia × Cattleya)**
Leptolaelia (Leptotes × Laelia)**
Lioponia (Broughtonia × Laeliopsis)**
Lowiara (Brassavola × Laelia × Sophronitis)***[1]
Luisanda (Luisia × Vanda)**
Lycasteria (Bifrenaria × Lycaste)**
Macomaria (Macodes × Haemaria)**
Miltonidium (Miltonia × Oncidium)**
Miltonioda (Miltonia × Cochlioda)**
Odontioda (Odontoglossum × Cochlioda)**
Odontobrassia (Odontoglossum × Brassia)**
Odontocidium (Odontoglossum × Oncidium)**
Odontonia (Odontoglossum × Miltonia)**
Oncidioda (Oncidium × Cochlioda)**
Opsilaelia (Laelia × Laeliopsis)**
Opsisanda (Vanda × Vandopsis)**
Pectabenaria (Pecteilis × Habenaria)**
Phaiocalanthe (Phaius × Calanthe)**
Phaiocymbidium (Phaius × Cymbidium)**
Phalandopsis (Vandopsis × Phalaenopsis)**
Phragmipaphiopedilum (Phragmipedium × Paphiopedilum)**
Potinara (Brassavola × Cattleya × Laelia × Sophronitis)****[1]
Renades (Aerides × Renanthera)**
Renanopsis (Renanthera × Vandopsis)**
Renanstylis (Renanthera × Rhynchostylis)**
Renantanda (Renanthera × Vanda)**
Renanthopsis (Renanthera × Phalaenopsis)**
Ridleyara (Arachnis × Trichoglottis × Vanda)***

Rodrettia (*Rodriguezia* × *Comparettia*)**

Rodricidium (*Rodriguezia* × *Oncidium*)**

Rolfeara (*Brassavola* × *Cattleya* × *Sophronitis*)***[1]

Sanderara (*Brassia* × *Odontoglossum* × *Cochlioda*)***

Sarcothera (*Sarcochilus* × *Renanthera*)**

Schombocattleya (*Schomburgkia* × *Cattleya*)**[3]

Schombodiacrium (*Schomburgkia* × *Diacrium*)**[2,3]

Schomboepidendrum (*Schomburgkia* × *Epidendrum*)**[3]

Schombolaelia (*Schomburgkia* × *Laelia*)**[3]

Sophrocattleya (*Sophronitis* × *Cattleya*)**

Sophrolaelia (*Sophronitis* × *Laelia*)**

Sophrolaeliocattleya (*Sophronitis* × *Laelia* × *Cattleya*)***

Spathophaius (*Spathoglottis* × *Phaius*)**

Tanakara (*Aerides* × *Phalaenopsis* × *Vanda*)***

Trichachnis (*Trichoglottis* × *Arachnis*)**

Trichocidium (*Trichocentrum* × *Oncidium*)**

Trichovanda (*Trichoglottis* × *Vanda*)**

Vancampe (*Vanda* × *Acampe*)**

Vandachnis (*Arachnis* × *Vandopsis*)**

Vandacostylis (*Vanda* × *Rhynchostylis*)**

Vandaenopsis (*Phalaenopsis* × *Vanda*)**

Vandofinetia (*Vanda* × *Neofinetia*)**

Vandopsides (*Aerides* × *Vandopsis*)**

Vuylstekeara (*Cochlioda* × *Miltonia* × *Odontoglossum*)***

Wilsonara (*Cochlioda* × *Odontoglossum* × *Oncidium*)***

Zygobatemania (*Zygopetalum* × *Batemania*)**

Zygocaste (*Zygopetalum* × *Lycaste*)**

Zygocolax (*Zygopetalum* × *Colax*)**

Zygonisia (*Zygopetalum* × *Aganisia*)**

Purposes of Hybridization

Orchid hybrids are produced for several reasons. Perhaps the most important is the creation of new color combinations, sizes, forms, or number of flowers produced. Hybridization is also practiced as a rather facile means of augmenting the quantity of plants (since vegetative propagation is at best an annoyingly slow and deliberate process), and also as a method for increasing the strength of a habitually weak-growing or sparse-flowering species, through combination with a more robust or floriferous one. Not all orchid genera (nor indeed, all species within a single genus) may be successfully crossed with one another, but in general those groups which are of close phylogenetic alliance are genetically compatible, and artificial hybrids may be induced. On pages 263 to 273 of this book, the reader will find lists of the genera in phylogenetic sequence. A certain amount of rather random experimental breeding has been carried out in recent times (notably in Hawaii and southern Florida) to ascertain exactly which

FRED A. STEWART, INC.

Cattleya x Tethys var. *Garnet Lake*

genera (or species within those genera) are compatible with which other ones, but the field is as yet largely unexplored. Tremendous numbers of fine and valuable species—and genera—have not been utilized at all by the breeders, and we may look forward, in future, to many new and wonderful artificial productions from enterprising orchidists.

Through hybridization it is often possible to secure plants that may be successfully cultivated in a region in which one or both of the parent species will not thrive. As an example, the magnificent "Waling-Waling" orchid of the Philippines, *Euanthe Sanderiana*, is grown only with difficulty in many areas, but large numbers of its hybrid forms (for example, *Vanda x Rothschildiana, Vanda x Manila,* and *Vanda x Tatzeri*—or *Vandanthe*) do very well in collections in these places.

In the more advanced hybrids, with several generations of breeding behind them, considerable variability usually occurs. A large part of the progeny is frequently of little value to the hybrid's originator, since it may not show the hoped-for characteristics of form and color and floriferousness sought in the cross. This explains the fluctuation in price of plants of the same cross offered for sale in the trade, since the really fine plants produced from a given hybrid are naturally of more intrinsic value than the mediocre or poor ones.

Naming of Hybrids

Fortunately for the orchidist's taxed brain, when orchid hybrids were first developed, it was decided that they should be given special names

Brassocattleya x John J. Mossman

The Orchid Journal

of their own, completely distinct from those of the various species orchids. Initially these new, artificially produced plants were named in honor of their originators, as, for example, *Calanthe x Dominyi.* As the number of orchid hybrids increased, however, it became necessary to invent new names to bestow on these plants, so that in contemporary times we have orchids named for almost everyone connected with the orchid family in any way, prominent personages of the time, geographic locales, anagrams of previous names, and even strictly inventive epithets bestowed by imaginative orchidists.

These names, once given to a hybrid, continue for any repeat cross made from the original parents. As an example, the hybrid between *Dendrobium heterocarpum* (usually listed under its synonym *D. aureum*) and *D. nobile* was, upon its registration by Ainsworth in 1874, given the name *Dendrobium x Ainsworthii*. Since that time all successive hybrids produced from these two parents have also been called *D. x Ainsworthii*. A cross between *D. nobile* var. *albiflorum* and *D. heterocarpum*, however, is given the name *D. x Ainsworthii* var.

Brassolaeliocattleya x Blanche Okamoto

WM. KIRCH—ORCHIDS, LTD.

Sanderae, and is a completely distinct plant from the typical *Dendrobium x Ainsworthii*.

Hybrids (or, more rarely, species) which have been designated as prize-winning forms by the various horticultural societies of the world which review fine plants are customarily indicated by initials, as follows: *Brassolaeliocattleya x Nugget*, AM, RHS (Award of Merit, Royal Horticultural Society), or *Cymbidium x eburneo-Lowianum* var. *concolor*, FCC, RHS (First Class Certificate, Royal Horticultural Society). These plants are of exceptional value, and are widely sought after as collectors' items and for utilization in further breeding.

Botanical vs. Horticultural Names

Brief note should be made here of the often annoying and now incredibly complex divergences between horticultural and botanical

nomenclature, as applied to orchid hybrids. At present, we are actually
dealing with two distinct systems of nomenclature—a botanically correct one, and one accepted generally by horticulturists and orchid
hybridists. An example is *Schomburgkia*, which is contemporarily
considered a mere section of *Laelia*. Yet we have such fully-registered
and rather frequently cultivated hybrids as those called Schombolaelias
and Schombocattleyas, which should, technically, be called Laelias and
Laeliocattleyas, respectively. This arrangement, however, would only
add materially to the already far too great confusion extant in the
naming of hybrids in this family of plants. We have, still further, the
relatively recent bigeneric cross *Schombodiacrium*, which contains
hybrids between *Schomburgkia* and *Diacrium*. As noted above, *Schomburgkia* is technically referable to *Laelia*, and *Diacrium* is now referred

Laeliocattleya x Biceps. This
is one of the new "unusual"
hybrids so popular with collectors everywhere.

WM. KIRCH—ORCHIDS, LTD.

to synonymic status under Rafinesque's genus *Caularthron*, hence we
have here an almost insoluble problem, one of a great many which
must eventually be taken up by the authorities dealing with such
situations in the nomenclature of the hybrid orchids. In this volume,
for the most part, such generally accepted hybrid names—although
they are patently incorrect, botanically—have been retained rather than
altering them to conform with botanical systems, to avoid any further
confusion.

One further example should be mentioned, since it involves a large
group of horticulturally important orchids, namely the so-called "labi-
ate" Cattleyas. In this aggregation, centering around *Cattleya labiata*,

certain specific names are currently in horticultural usage which have no standing botanically. For instance, such so-called "species" of this alliance, such as *C. Mossiae, C. Dowiana, C. Trianaei*, etc., are botanically mere variants of the widespread and polymorphic *C. labiata*. Thus the correct names for these orchids (which are utilized throughout this work) are, respectively, *Cattleya labiata* var. *Mossiae, C. labiata* var. *Dowiana*, and *C. labiata* var. *Trianaei*. Here again, however, no purpose would be served by altering the registrations of the hundreds upon hundreds of hybrids incorporating these and other confused species (or variants) in their parentage.

MECHANICS OF HYBRIDIZATION

The mechanics of hybridization in the orchids are basically simple, more so than in many other groups of flowering plants. The sexual apparatus of all orchids, as has been pointed out previously, is borne on a fleshy finger-like structure called the column or gynostemium, situated at the center of the flower. This column bears the pollen (in most orchids arranged into compact masses termed pollinia) in a small but intricate case near the apex. Below this, almost always on the underside, is the stigma, or stigmatic surface, which—when mature and ready for fertilization—is sticky and moist to the touch.

Selecting the Parents

In making a hybrid, the first thing the breeder should do is to appraise the parent plants to be crossed. Amateurs too often fall into the habit of indiscriminately hybridizing every plant that comes into flower in their collections. Not only will many of these random crosses not "take" (that is, viable seed will not be produced, even though the capsule may often swell and develop, much in the normal manner), but even if good seed is produced, and the seedlings are taken on their slow, tedious journey to maturity, highly inferior, often completely worthless plants may result. There are already far too many poor hybrids in orchid collections, and the amateur accomplishes absolutely nothing—other than to waste several years of his time and effort and growing space—by haphazardly making crosses.

The orchidist may wish to make a new hybrid, one that has never been made before, hence one that is not registered in the *Hybrid Lists*. Or he may wish to remake a desirable cross already recorded. Both

Laeliocattleya x Buccaneer 'Purple Flame'

FRED A. STEWART, INC.

of the parent plants should be especially fine ones, robust and strong vegetatively, with flowers of fine quality.

Storing Pollinia

If a plant in flower is to be bred with another that flowers at a later period, the pollinia may be safely stored (sometimes for several months, without decreased potency) for future use. The diminutive pollen-masses should be carefully removed from their anther-case, wrapped in a small square of tissue paper, and placed in a vial or tube; a large number of these tubes may be stored in a covered jar, in the bottom of which—but kept from contact with the pollinia—some crystals of calcium chloride are placed to reduce the moisture content, and thus inhibit formation of mildew and mold. Seed may also be stored in this way; sometimes (in exceptional cases) it retains its viability for as long as six years. The storage jar should be kept in a refrigerated place at all times. Some persons suggest sealing the individual tubes in which the pollinia or seed are stored, with paraffin, and this seems beneficial. Contents of each tube should be labeled with full name of the plant, date collected, and original quantity (in the case of the pollen-masses). The viability of stored pollinia and seed decreases rapidly; therefore they should, under all circumstances, be used as soon as possible after collection.

Procedure for Pollination

The actual mechanical operation of cross-pollination of orchids is remarkably simple. A whittled-down match stick or the larger end of

Odontioda x Cetionette. This fine hybrid is a cross between an *Odontoglossum* and a *Cochlioda.*

J. E. DOWNWARD

a flattened toothpick may be used with facility. This instrument is inserted under the edge of the anther-cap; by slight pressure, the sticky stalks of the pollinia (usually called *caudicles*) attach themselves to this, and the pollinia may be withdrawn. A piece of paper or the palm of the hand should be held under the column during this operation, to catch one of the tiny pollen-masses, should it accidentally be dropped.

Pollinia should never be touched, if possible, with the fingers or with any dirty implement or surface.

Once the pollinia are obtained, all that is necessary to effect pollination is to carefully place all of the little yellow or whitish pieces on the surface of the stigma of the female parent. They will adhere, because of the stigma's viscous character. All of each individual pollen-mass (or *pollinium*, as the individual piece is technically called) should be in intimate contact with this surface, not with only part of it. When the full complement of pollen-masses (that is, four in *Cattleya* and *Epidendrum*, eight in *Laelia*, etc.) is too large to fit on the stigmatic surface of a smaller flower, the number of pollinia placed on the stigma may be reduced proportionately. Because of an obvious mechanical characteristic of the pollen-tubes produced by these germinating pollinia, it is necessary to place the pollen-masses from the larger of two given flowers (the one which produces, therefore, generally the larger pollinia) on the stigma of the smaller, else the tubes will not reach the ovules and no fertilized seed will result. It is always essential to remove the pollinia from the flower being pollinated, to assure that no danger of mixed pollinia may occur. Putting more than one kind of pollen on the same stigma should never be attempted. The result would be a mixture of hybrid offspring, the correct classification of which would be impossible.

Technique for "Lady's-Slippers"

All orchidaceous plants are hybridized in this fashion, except for the "Lady's-Slippers," the members of the subtribe *Cypripedilinae—Paphiopedilum, Phragmipedium,* and *Cypripedium* (the fourth genus of this aggregation, *Selenipedium,* is not in cultivation, and has not been used in hybrid work). These orchids, probably the most archaic of all extant types, differ in the column structure from all others in the family, as explained on page 23. Instead of a single fertile anther, as in all other orchids, these have two. A third anther is also present, but this is a sterile structure and is considerably altered, so that it forms a shield-shaped body, called a staminode or staminodium, on the front of the column. The two fertile anthers, with their rather mealy or granular pollen, are found on the sides of the column, beneath and in back of this staminode. The sticky stigma, rather similar in appearance to that of other kinds of orchids, lies about midway between these two lateral anthers. Pollination is effected in much the same way as that described above. *All* available pollen should be used, since its germination rate is rather low. The pollen of the "Lady's-Slippers" should be used immediately after removal from the flower, since it will not tolerate storage for any lengthy period. A proportionately small amount of seed is generally produced by these orchids, and their germination is often a relatively difficult task.

Paphiopedilum x Maudiae

ROD MC LELLAN COMPANY

After Pollination

If the plants used to make the cross are treated as outlined above, and if they are genetically compatible, the ovary of the pollinated flower will start to enlarge within a few days, generally inside of a week. The blossom will have wilted by this time (in most cases, though species such as *Phalaenopsis Lueddemanniana* have a persistent perianth which thickens and even increases in size after fertilization), and virtually all color will have drained from the floral segments. Many orchidists carefully clip the sepals, petals, and lip from around the column, leaving about half an inch of floral tissue, as soon as the flower has been pollinated. This is designed to prevent molding or mildewing from the possibly rotting flower parts.

The seed capsule (often incorrectly called the seed pod) which gradually forms from this swollen ovary finally matures anywhere from six months (sooner in certain terrestrial species) to well over a year after fertilization. As soon as it starts to become yellowish or brownish (a sign of incipient splitting of the sutures, to permit release of the mature seeds), a paper or cellophane bag should be tied around it—not tightly, since the stalk is very brittle—to prevent loss of the seed. The mature capsule should be removed from the plant as soon as the first split occurs in one of the grooves along its sides, and placed in a

Renanthera x Brookie Chandler

cool dry place until it has completely split open and the seed may be conveniently removed.

Seed should be taken from the capsule with a sterilized instrument, as it is liable to contamination at any stage. A small sample should be critically examined under a microscope to ascertain its degree of vitality. Those seeds which contain a plump greenish or brownish proembryo within the intricate weblike shell may be considered good ones, while those without the proembryo or with a small shriveled one are of no value. The higher the percentage of seeds with pro-embryos, naturally the higher proportion of germination to be expected when they are sown. The number of flasks or tubes sown can be regulated according to the viability of the seed utilized.

Keeping the Plant Strong

While the seed-capsule is ripening, particular attention should be paid to the cultural wants of the plant. It should be given an especially well ventilated position in the house, adequate but not excessive water, and a suitable quantity of light and heat. If the foliage or pseudobulbs become shriveled or show any signs of serious weakness, it is safer to cut off the capsule, since the plant's life may otherwise be endangered. The production of a seed-capsule is a drain on the strength of any orchid, and may slow its normal growth cycle measurably. This growth is customarily resumed the season after removal of the mature seed-capsule or, for some species, after a brief resting period.

APPENDIX

NAMES AND CLASSIFICATION

If the beginner spends a little time studying the names applied to his prize plants, he will come to realize that they are not only interesting, but highly instructive, since in most cases they give some idea about the plant itself, its affinity, or its history.

"Common" or vernacular names are of scant value when one is dealing with the thousands of members, both hybrids and species, of the Orchidaceae. Few common names have been assigned to these myriad plants, and such confusing duplications have arisen among those few that their value is nil. Therefore, it is essential that the orchidist know his plants by their correct botanical names. Their pronunciation becomes easy with practice and use.

For purposes of classification, all orchids—and all other plants as well—are given a basic name consisting of two units. For example, in the name *Cattleya labiata*, the word *Cattleya* denotes a group, or *genus*, of closely related *species*. *Cattleya* corresponds to the surname of a person, whereas the second name, *labiata*, refers to a particular kind of *Cattleya* and corresponds to a person's given name. Although usually not so written in popular works, the entire name would correctly and completely be *Cattleya labiata* Ldl., the "Ldl." being an accepted abbreviation for John Lindley, the noted British orchidologist who first described this species of orchid as new to science.

The correct family name for *all* orchids is *Orchidaceae*, a word which should always be spelled with a capital letter, as given here. To state that an orchid is a member of "the *Laelia* family" or "the *Dendrobium* family" is incorrect. In orchids these allied groups of genera (together with their component species) are called *subtribes*, and the correct names to be applied to these two aggregations would be, respectively, the *Laeliinae* and the *Dendrobiinae*.

A generic name, such as *Cattleya*, is always spelled with a capital letter. The specific names—those relating to the species, as, for example, *labiata*—may under contemporary rules of botanical nomenclature be spelled with a small letter. Many botanists, however, and many orchidists as well, follow the old, well-established system of variable rulings with regard to the capitalization of the initial letter of specific names, and in this book we have followed the original method of spelling certain specific epithets with a capital initial.

In addition to the generic and specific names, an orchid may have a third, or *varietal*, name, given to a phase which is somewhat different from the typical one, but not sufficiently distinct to require full rank as a species. Varietal names are likely to be based on such superficial and, relatively unimportant characteristics botanically, as color or slight difference in size or shape. Thus we have *Dendrobium fimbriatum* var. *oculatum*, which is a form of *D. fimbriatum* with a brown eye, or spot, on the lip. Subvarieties—abbreviated *subvar.*—also are found in the Orchidaceae. These are lesser variants, placed in status beneath the true varieties, which are in turn placed under the species; a well-known example is *Cattleya labiata* var. *Dowiana* subvar. *aurea*, which is the Colombian phase of the magnificent orchid usually known in horticulture (though erroneously) as *Cattleya Dowiana* var. *aurea* or *Cattleya aurea*. Forms—correctly written as *forma*, often abbreviated *fma.*—are very minor color variations which occur in many orchidaceous plants, a good example being *Cattleya labiata* var. *Mossiae* fma. *Reineckeana*, an epithet almost universally and incorrectly written as *Cattleya Mossiae* var. *Reineckeana* or even as *Cattleya Reineckeana*. The practice of omitting the highly significant designating words between the various parts of the orchid name—such as writing *Cattleya Mossiae Reineckeana* or *Cattleya labiata Dowiana*—is to be avoided, since it is patently incorrect and causes confusion. A further error often committed by orchidists is the writing or oral mention of a species without any indication of its genus, such as "*Papilio*," which would to most enthusiasts signify *Oncidium Papilio*, but which might just as well refer to *Dendrobium Papilio*.

The rules covering orchid species apply in the main to the hybrids as well. Hybrid plants of all sorts, however, are correctly indicated by the insertion of a small letter *x* between the generic and specific names, as *Cattleya x Enid*. A cross between two species (or two species-variations) is correctly designated by the use of a multiplication symbol between the parents' names, as *Cattleya intermedia* × *Cattleya Skinneri*. Hybrid names are not correctly written, unless they have this designating *x* between the two parts which comprise them, since this is often the only immediate way we have of knowing whether or not they are of hybrid origin. Because these rules have not always been followed, the nomenclature of hybrid orchids, despite the work done by the official registrars toward the recording of all orchid crosses, is in a state of great confusion.

The scientific classification of orchids is an interesting and generally neglected topic. Most professional orchidologists spend a large part of their time working with dried specimens of orchids which have been collected by amateur or commercial botanists or explorers in the wild. These dried specimens are called *herbarium specimens* or *sheets*. A quantity of them taken together forms a *herbarium*. Most herbaria (the plural form) are not devoted exclusively to one group of plants, such as the orchids, but contain dried materials representative of all types of plants, from fungi to daisies. A few of these herbaria, however—notably some private ones—contain only orchid specimens; the world-famed Oakes Ames Orchid Herbarium, now deposited at Harvard University, has more than 60,000 sheets of orchid plants and flowers, plus large collections of materials kept in alcohol or other preservatives. A few large herbaria throughout the world possess more than one million sheets, and virtually every educational or research institution boasts at least a modest herbarium, in which some orchid sheets are deposited.

When the orchidologist sees a new dried specimen that has been collected in, for example, Colombia, chances are that it will not have a name attached to it. Most collectors of plants cannot take the time while they are in the field—nor do they have the facilities there—to classify the specimens they gather. Hence the job of the orchidologist is to find the correct name for the plant on the herbarium sheet in front of him.

Since the family is such a tremendous and complicated one, certain orchidologists specialize, through mutual international agreement, in the orchid floras of a particular country or area, or in a particular genus or group of genera. Specimens needing identification are therefore forwarded to the specialists in the particular field. Finding the name of the specimen occasionally proves a simple job; but more frequently it will require hours —sometimes even days—of intensive research and study. The specialist must often follow a complicated series of steps before reaching a critical decision. Usually, unless the genus represented is particularly rare (or even previously unknown), the orchidologist has some idea of its identity, at least as to genus; if not, however, he must go through the entire phylogenetical system of the Orchidaceae (see pages 263 to 273) to determine the plant's relationships.

Vegetative characters of the plant before him, coupled with the appearance of the inflorescence, number of flowers, their arrangement, etc., and the place of origin of the collected specimen, give him some clues to its identity. But to be sure he must usually remove a flower from the spike for more detailed examination and comparison. (This flower will be crushed flat, completely dried out, and usually of a dirty brown or black hue— since most orchids lose their floral color when being preserved for the herbarium—and almost completely unrecognizable to the layman as even a representative of the Orchidaceae!) The dry flower is placed in a small beaker of water and gently boiled for a brief period, until the parts have become soft and pliable. Under a dissecting microscope, the botanist carefully teases the flower apart, sepal by sepal, petal by petal, taking care that he does not mutilate the blossom's parts. Usually the column is the most critical portion of the orchid flower for determination of the species, but the shape and size of the sepals, petals, and lip, any protuberances such as calli, lamellae, or keels on the lip, and innumerable other minute characters also must enter into his consideration. If the plant is still unknown to him, after this dissection and microscopic inspection, he must compare it with specimens and descriptions of allied plants.

A comprehensive reference library of books, magazines, articles, and other materials is essential to this work. Often, however, it is impossible to establish a plant's identity from fragmentary descriptions in the literature. In such a case, the orchidologist must look elsewhere for reference materials, probably in the form of herbarium sheets of specimens previously determined, for comparison with the plant he is studying.

The individual specimen on which an orchid species (or variety or form) is originally based—and from which its initial published description is drawn—is called the *type specimen* or *type sheet*. These valuable types are scattered in all of the herbaria of the world, wherever a specialist happens to be working. Sometimes the orchidologist may arrange to borrow the one necessary (or a duplicate of it) for his study. With this original record at hand he may be able to determine his puzzling specimen—or perhaps not!

Finally, if all possible avenues of study have been exhausted, he will probably assume that the specimen before him represents a new species, or possibly even a new genus of orchid. He carefully records the most minute details and measurements of the specimen, preferably makes a diagnostic drawing of the plant and all of the floral parts, and composes a diagnosis of the new species, which must, under botanical regulations, be written in Latin, the universal language of science. Most orchidologists also append a more comprehensive description in English (or German or French or Portuguese or any other language) as well, giving only the essential differentiating details in Latin. The specialist then arranges to have this description and illustration published in a recognized authoritative periodical or book; he puts the established name of the species on the label of the herbarium sheet, indicates his own name and the date of identification, and the job is done—unless some other orchidologist decides that the new species (or genus) is not a valid one, and wishes to argue the technicalities of the point.

The name that the orchidologist gives to his new species (or genus) is a matter of individual choice. If he wishes to honor the collector of the specimen, he may name the species accordingly, as Ames and Correll did for the handsome *Cattleya Pachecoi*, first gathered by Don Mariano Pacheco H. in the Department of Suchitepéquez in Guatemala. If the person being honored did not actually gather the plant being named for him, it customarily receives a slightly different termination to the name, such as *Cattleya x Hardyana*, a natural hybrid which was not actually collected by William Hardy in its native Colombia, but which first flowered in his collection in England; if Hardy had personally found the plant in the wild, its name would probably have been "*Hardyi*."

Should the orchidologist decide that a descriptive name would be more appropriate for his new species, he may come upon some particular characteristic of the plant, flower, habitat or other feature for his epithet. Thus we find *Pleione humilis*, the specific name of which signifies "humble" or "dwarf" and describes its small stature; *Catasetum viridiflavum*, meaning "greenish-yellow," and referring to the color of the flowers; *Epidendrum ibaguense*, meaning "from Ibagué," in reference to the particular region in Colombia where the species was first collected by Ruiz and Pavón; or *Bulbophyllum minutissimum*, meaning "most minute," and referring to the tiny size of the plant.

If the orchidologist is preparing a monograph or a revision of a particular genus or group of species within a genus, he must often study hundreds or thousands of herbarium specimens, together with available literature, illustrations, unpublished records that he is able to acquire, and other pertinent materials. This procedure also applies to the compilation of an orchid flora for a given region. Here, too, thousands of individual specimens must be examined and critically studied before any work of this nature can become authoritative.

PHYLOGENETIC LIST OF THE ORCHIDACEAE

The following phylogenetical list of the genera comprising the Orchidaceae is based upon the system proposed by Rudolf Schlechter in 1926 (in *Notizbl. Bot. Gart. Berlin* 9(88): 567–590.). As is natural, since that time numerous alterations have been made in the Schlechterian system. These have been incorporated in the arrangement that follows.

The genera are placed according to their theoretical degree of development, commencing with the ancient and highly aberrant "Lady's-Slippers" of the subtribe *Cypripedilinae*, and terminating with the very complex, often leafless, epiphytic plants comprising the subtribe *Campylocentrinae*. Within the various subtribal groupings, the genera are arranged insofar as possible to show their relationship (or presumed relationship) one to the other. Whenever the precise position of a given genus is open to doubt, this entry is followed by a question-mark in parentheses.

In some instances, one or more genera are separated from those above by a broken line. This is done because their exact position within the subtribe is in doubt. When they are also followed by a parenthetical question-mark, there may be some doubt as to their retention in that subtribe.

A grand total of 668 genera in 88 subtribes are indicated as being presumably valid in the system proposed below. Of these, eight genera are placed at the end of the lists, designated "Subtribe Not Determined." These are so marked because, as of the time of publication of this volume, no critical information concerning them has been available.

SUBTRIBE CYPRIPEDILINAE
1. *Selenipedium* Rchb.f.
2. *Cypripedium* L.
3. *Phragmipedium* Rolfe
4. *Paphiopedilum* Pfitz.

SUBTRIBE HABENARINAE
(Group Platanthereae)
5. *Ophrys* L.
6. *Serapias* L.
7. *Aceratorchis* Schltr.

SUBTRIBE HABENARINAE
(Group Platanthereae)
8. *Aceras* R.Br.
9. *Himantoglossum* Spreng.
10. *Anacamptis* A. Rich.
11. *Neotinea* Rchb.f.
12. *Steveniella* Schltr.
13. *Orchis* [Tournef.] L.
14. *Holothrix* L. C. Rich.
15. *Deroemeria* Rchb.f.
16. *Bartholina* R.Br.
17. *Neobolusia* Schltr.
18. *Silvorchis* J.J.Sm.
19. *Schwartzkopffia* Krzl.
20. *Brachycorythis* Ldl.
21. *Diplacorchis* Schltr.
22. *Traunsteinera* Rchb.
23. *Nigritella* L. C. Rich.
24. *Neottianthe* Schltr.
25. *Tsaiorchis* Tang & Wang (?)
26. *Amitostigma* Schltr.
27. *Schizochilus* Sond.
28. *Rolfeella* Schltr.
29. *Platanthera* Ldl.
30. *Hemipilia* Ldl.

----

31. *Chusua* Nevski
32. *Parhabenaria* Gagnep.
33. *Porolabium* Tang & Wang
34. *Smithorchis* Tang & Wang
35. *Stevenorchis* Wankow & Krzl. (?)
36. *Symphyosepalum* Hand.-Mazz. (?)

(Group Habenarieae)
37. *Tylostigma* Schltr.
38. *Herminium* R.Br.
39. *Pecteilis* Raf.
40. *Peristylus* Bl.
41. *Benthamia* A. Rich.
42. *Stenoglottis* Ldl.
43. *Arnottia* A. Rich.
44. *Cynosorchis* Thou.
45. *Platycoryne* Rchb.f.
46. *Physoceras* Schltr.
47. *Bonatea* Willd.

48. *Habenaria* Willd.
49. *Gymnadenia* R.Br.
50. *Megalorchis* Perr.
51. *Diplomeris* D.Don
52. *Roeperocharis* Rchb.f.
53. *Centrostigma* Schltr.

----

54. *Podandria* Rolfe

SUBTRIBE ANDROCORYDINAE
55. *Androcorys* Schltr.

SUBTRIBE HUTTONAEINAE
56. *Huttonaea* Harv.

SUBTRIBE DISINAE
57. *Schizodium* Ldl.
58. *Disa* Berg.
59. *Monadenia* Ldl.
60. *Penthea* Ldl.
61. *Forficaria* Ldl.
62. *Herschelia* Ldl.
63. *Orthopenthea* Rolfe
64. *Amphigena* Rolfe
65. *Brownleea* Harv.

SUBTRIBE SATYRIINAE
66. *Pachites* Ldl.
67. *Satyrium* L.
68. *Satyridium* Ldl.

SUBTRIBE DISPERIDINAE
69. *Pterygodium* Sw.
70. *Corycium* Sw.
71. *Ommatodium* Ldl.
72. *Ceratandra* Eckl.
73. *Anochilus* Rolfe
74. *Ceratandropsis* Rolfe
75. *Evota* Rolfe
76. *Disperis* Sw.

SUBTRIBE PTEROSTYLIDINAE
77. *Pterostylis* R.Br.

SUBTRIBE DIURIDINAE
78. *Orthoceras* R.Br.
79. *Diuris* R.Br.

SUBTRIBE THELYMITRINAE
80. *Thelymitra* Forst.
81. *Epiblema* R.Br.
82. *Calochilus* R.Br.

SUBTRIBE PRASOPHYLLINAE
83. *Microtis* R.Br.
84. *Goadbyella* R.S.Rog.
85. *Prasophyllum* R.Br.
86. *Corunastylis* Fitzg.

SUBTRIBE DRAKAEINAE
87. *Chiloglottis* R.Br.
88. *Caleana* R.Br.
89. *Drakaea* Ldl.
90. *Spiculaea* Ldl.

SUBTRIBE CALADENIINAE
91. *Glossodia* R.Br.
92. *Eriochilus* R.Br.
93. *Rimacola* Rupp
94. *Caladenia* R.Br.
95. *Aporostylis* Rupp & Hatch
96. *Petalochilus* R.S.Rog.
97. *Adenochilus* Hk.f.
98. *Codonorchis* Ldl.

SUBTRIBE ACIANTHINAE
99. *Acianthus* R.Br.
100. *Townsonia* Cheesem.
101. *Stigmatodactylus* Maxim.
102. *Lyperanthus* R.Br.
103. *Burnettia* Ldl.

SUBTRIBE CORYBASINAE
104. *Corybas* Salisb.

SUBTRIBE CRYPTOSTYLIDINAE
105. *Coilochilus* Schltr.
106. *Cryptostylis* R.Br.
107. *Chlorosa* Bl.

SUBTRIBE PACHYPLECTRO-
NINAE
108. *Pachyplectron* Schltr.

SUBTRIBE MEGASTYLIDINAE
109. *Megastylis* Schltr.

SUBTRIBE CHLORAEINAE
110. *Chloraea* Ldl.
111. *Bipinnula* Ldl.

SUBTRIBE LISTERINAE
112. *Listera* R.Br.
113. *Neottia* Sw.
114. *Holopogon* Kom. & Nevski
115. *Vieillardorchis* Krzl.

SUBTRIBE CEPHALANTHERINAE
116. *Aphyllorchis* Bl.
117. *Evrardia* Gagnep.
118. *Epipactis* [Zinn., in part] Sw.
119. *Cephalanthera* L.C.Rich.
120. *Limodorum* Sw.

SUBTRIBE VANILLINAE
121. *Pogoniopsis* Rchb.f.
122. *Triphora* Nutt.
123. *Monophyllorchis* Schltr.
124. *Xerorchis* Schltr.
125. *Isotria* Raf.
126. *Pogonia* Juss.
127. *Psilochilus* B.-R.
128. *Cleistes* L.C.Rich.
129. *Vanilla* Sw.
130. *Galeola* Lour.
131. *Epistephium* Kth.
132. *Duckeella* Porto & Brade
133. *Lecanorchis* Bl.

SUBTRIBE SOBRALIINAE
134. *Elleanthus* Presl
135. *Sobralia* R. & P.
136. *Diceratostele* Summerh.

SUBTRIBE BLETILLINAE
137. *Arethusa* [Gronov.] L.
138. *Eleorchis* Maekawa
139. *Crybe* Ldl.
140. *Bletilla* Rchb.f.
141. *Calopogon* R.Br.
----
142. *Arethusantha* Finet (?)

SUBTRIBE NERVILIINAE
143. *Nervilia* Comm. ex Gaud.

SUBTRIBE BRACHTIINAE
498. *Brachtia* Rchb.f.

SUBTRIBE TRICHOPILIINAE
499. *Trichopilia* Ldl.
500. *Helcia* Ldl.
501. *Oliveriana* Rchb.f.

SUBTRIBE COCHLIODINAE
502. *Cochlioda* Ldl.
503. *Binotia* Rolfe

SUBTRIBE ONCIDIINAE
504. *Gomesa* R.Br.
505. *Hellerorchis* A.D.Hawkes
506. *Mesospinidium* Ldl.
507. *Neodryas* Rchb.f.
508. *Amparoa* Schltr.
509. *Odontoglossum* HBK
510. *Symphyglossum* Schltr.
511. *Aspasia* Ldl.
512. *Systeloglossum* Schltr.
513. *Ada* Ldl.
514. *Brassia* R.Br.
515. *Caucaea* Schltr.
516. *Miltonia* Ldl.
517. *Palumbina* Rchb.f.
518. *Oncidium* Sw.
519. *Solenidium* Ldl.
520. *Erycina* Ldl.
521. *Leochilus* Kn. & Westc.
522. *Sigmatostalix* Rchb.f.
523. *Ornithophora* B.-R.
524. *Hofmeisterella* Rchb.f.

SUBTRIBE LOCKHARTIINAE
525. *Lockhartia* Hk.

SUBTRIBE ORNITHOCEPHA-
LINAE
526. *Phymatidium* Ldl.
527. *Platyrhiza* B.-R.
528. *Hintonella* Ames
529. *Chytroglossa* Rchb.f.
530. *Dipteranthus* B.-R.
531. *Ornithocephalus* Hk.

532. *Oakes-Amesia* Schweinf. &
Allen
533. *Cordanthera* L.O.Wms.
534. *Zygostates* Ldl.
535. *Thysanoglossa* Porto & Brade
536. *Sphyrastylis* Schltr.

SUBTRIBE SAUNDERSIINAE
537. *Saundersia* Rchb.f.

SUBTRIBE PAPPERITZIINAE
538. *Papperitzia* Rchb.f.
539. *Polyotidium* Garay

SUBTRIBE NOTYLIINAE
540. *Notylia* Ldl.
541. *Cryptarrhena* R.Br. ex Ldl.
542. *Macradenia* R.Br.
543. *Warmingia* Rchb.f.

SUBTRIBE TELIPOGONINAE
544. *Telipogon* HBK
545. *Trichoceros* HBK
546. *Sodiroella* Schltr.
547. *Dipterostele* Schltr.
548. *Stellilabium* Schltr.

SUBTRIBE DICHAEINAE
549. *Dichaea* Ldl.

SUBTRIBE PACHYPHYLLINAE
550. *Pachyphyllum* Ldl.
551. *Centropetalum* Ldl.

SUBTRIBE PTEROSTEMMATINAE
552. *Pterostemma* Lehm. & Krzl.

SUBTRIBE SARCANTHINAE
(Group Sarcochileae)
553. *Calymmanthera* Schltr.
554. *Chamaeanthus* Schltr.
555. *Thrixspermum* Lour.
556. *Bogoria* J.J.Sm.
557. *Chiloschista* Ldl.
558. *Drymonanthus* Nicholls
559. *Sarcochilus* R.Br.
560. *Ascochilopsis* Carr

SUBTRIBE SARCANTHINAE
(Group Sarcochileae)
561. *Rhinerrhiza* Rupp
562. *Chroniochilus* J.J.Sm.
563. *Peristeranthus* T.E.Hunt
564. *Ornithochilus* Wall.
565. *Aerides* Lour.
566. *Macropodanthus* L.O.Wms.
567. *Rhynchostylis* Bl.
568. *Phalaenopsis* Bl.
569. *Paraphalaenopsis* A.D. Hawkes

----

570. *Cheirorchis* Carr
571. *Biermannia* King & Pantl.

(Group Podangeae)
572. *Rhipidoglossum* Schltr.
573. *Podangis* Schltr.
574. *Aeranthes* Ldl.

(Group Vandeae)
575. *Adenoncos* Bl.
576. *Luisia* Gaud.
577. *Cottonia* Wight
578. *Diploprora* Hk.f.
579. *Vanda* Jones
580. *Euanthe* Schltr.
581. *Vandopsis* Pfitz.
582. *Arachnis* Bl.
583. *Dimorphorchis* Rolfe
584. *Armodorum* Breda
585. *Renanthera* Lour.
586. *Renantherella* Ridl.
587. *Ascoglossum* Schltr.
588. *Ascocentrum* Schltr.

(Group Angraeceae)
589. *Bonniera* Cordem.
590. *Jumellea* Schltr.
591. *Angraecum* Bory
592. *Ypsilopus* Summerh.
593. *Ambrella* H.Perr.
594. *Oeoniella* Schltr.
595. *Oeonia* Ldl.
596. *Cryptopus* Ldl.
597. *Sobennikoffia* Schltr.

598. *Perrierella* Schltr.
599. *Lemurella* Schltr.
600. *Neobathiea* Schltr.

----

601. *Dinklageella* Mansf.

(Group Saccolabieae)
602. *Dryadorchis* Schltr.
603. *Saccolabium* Bl.
604. *Saccolabiopsis* J.J.Sm.
605. *Omoea* Bl.
606. *Gastrochilus* D.Don
607. *Holcoglossum* Schltr.
608. *Neofinetia* Hu
609. *Pennilabium* J.J.Sm.
610. *Acampe* Ldl.
611. *Malleola* J.J.Sm. & Schltr.
612. *Uncifera* Ldl.
613. *Porphyrodesme* Schltr.
614. *Robiquetia* Gaud.
615. *Abdominea* J.J.Sm.
616. *Schoenorchis* Bl.
617. *Phragmorchis* L.O.Wms.
618. *Sarcanthus* Ldl.
619. *Mobilabium* Rupp
620. *Camarotis* Ldl.
621. *Pomatocalpa* Breda
622. *Pelatantheria* Ridl.
623. *Trichoglottis* Bl. emend. Rchb.f.
624. *Diplocentrum* Ldl.
625. *Hymenorchis* Schltr.
626. *Geissanthera* Schltr.
627. *Microtatorchis* Schltr.
628. *Taeniophyllum* Bl.
629. *Microsaccus* Bl.
630. *Ceratochilus* Bl.

(Group Aerangeae)
631. *Listrostachys* Rchb.f.
632. *Microcoelia* Ldl.
633. *Taeniorrhiza* Summerh.
634. *Chauliodon* Summerh.
635. *Ankylocheilos* Summerh.
636. *Encheiridion* Summerh.
637. *Lemurorchis* Krzl.
638. *Diaphananthe* Schltr.

(Group Aerangeae)
639. *Sarcorhynchus* Schltr.
640. *Bolusiella* Schltr.
641. *Chamaeangis* Schltr.
642. *Plectrelminthus* Raf.
643. *Aerangis* Rchb.f.
644. *Barombia* Schltr.
645. *Mystacidium* Ldl.
646. *Cyrtorchis* Schltr.
647. *Solenangis* Schltr.
648. *Eurychone* Schltr.
649. *Ancistrorhynchus* Finet
650. *Angraecopsis* Krzl.
651. *Tridactyle* Schltr.
652. *Eggelingia* Summerh.

- -

653. *Nephrangis* [Schltr]. Summerh. (?)
654. *Rangaeris* [Schltr.] Summerh. (?)

655. *Sphyrarhynchus* Mansf. (?)
656. *Triceratorhynchus* Summerh. (?)
657. *Tuberolabium* Yamamoto (?)

SUBTRIBE CAMPYLOCENTRINAE
658. *Campylocentrum* Bth.
659. *Polyrrhiza* Pfitz.
660. *Dendrophylax* Rchb.f.

(SUBTRIBE NOT DETERMINED)
661. *Changnienia* Chien
662. *Cordiglottis* J.J.Sm.
663. *Donacopsis* Gagnep.
664. *Forbesina* Ridl.
665. *Hakoneaste* Mak.
666. *Neoclemensia* Carr
667. *Thylacis* Gagnep.
668. *Zetagyne* Ridl.

GLOSSARY

Acuminate: tapering to a sharp point.

Acute: ending sharply and abruptly, in an angle of less than 90°.

Adnate: grown to; said of parts that are attached throughout their entire length to parts of a different series.

Adventitious: produced out of the usual or normal place.

Alate: winged; having wings or winglike parts or extensions.

Anther: the sac containing the pollen, *i.e.*, the essential portion of the stamen or male part of the flower.

Anther-cap: in orchids, the covering of the pollen-masses on the flower's column.

Aphid: plant louse.

Aphis: a genus of plant lice.

Apical: pertaining to the top or apex.

Ascending: upcurved; growing or directed upward.

Asymbiotic: pertaining to growth without the use of symbiotic fungi, particularly in reference to orchid seed-growing.

Attenuate: becoming slender or very narrow; slenderly long-tapering.

Auricle: an earlike appendage.

Bifid: split in two to the middle; divided into two equal lobes.

Bigeneric: having members of two distinct genera in the parentage; applied to hybrids.

Bilobed: two-lobed; parted into two lobes.

Bisexual: two-sexed; having both stamens and pistils in the same flower.

Blade: expanded portion of a leaf or petal.

"Botanical": when used in reference to orchids, a term designating any species (or genus) which is technically not grown commercially for its flowers. "Botanical" orchids, however, may be of great interest to collectors, and widely cultivated by them.

Bract: a much-reduced leaflike or scalelike organ subtending a flower or aggregation of flowers; a modified inflorescence leaf.

Bracteate: bearing bracts.

Caespitose: growing in tufts or dense clumps.

Callus: a hard prominence or protuberance. Plural—*calli.*

Calyx: Outer series of the floral envelope; the sepals as a unit. This term is rarely used in reference to orchid sepals.

Campanulate: bell-shaped.

Capsule: a dry splitting seed-vessel composed of two or more parts (carpels). The "seed-pods" of orchids are correctly termed capsules.

Cauda: a more or less elongate tail-like growth or projection. Plural—*caudae.*

Caudate: furnished with a tail or tails.

Caudicle: in orchids, the stalk of the pollinium.

Ciliate: fringed, usually with small hairs.

Claw: long, narrow, stalklike base of petals, sepals, or lip, found in some orchid flowers.

Clawed: furnished with a claw.

Clinandrium: the usually rather cup-shaped area of the column's apex of the orchid flower, in which the anther lies.

Column: the specialized central body of the flower in orchids, formed by the union of the stamens and pistil; gynostemium.

Cordate: heart-shaped.

Coriaceous: leathery in texture.

Corm: a solid, bulblike structure, usually subterranean.

Corolla: the interior perianth of a flower, composed of the petals. This term is rarely used in reference to the petals of an orchid flower.

Crested: with elevated and irregular or toothed ridges.

Cuneate: wedge-shaped; triangular, with the narrow end at the point of attachment.

Deciduous: falling off, as the leaves of certain orchids at maturity.

Decurved: curved downward.

Deflexed: bent or turned down or away, usually rather abruptly.

Deltoid: triangular; shaped like the Greek letter *delta.*

Dentate: with sharp-pointed teeth directed outward from the margin.

Denticulate: minutely dentate.

Dimorphic: having two dissimilar forms.

Disc: a more or less rounded, flattened structure; in orchids, particularly referring to the median or basal portion of the labellum (usually the midlobe).

Distichous: arranged in two rows or ranks.

Elliptic: oval and equally narrowed to rounded ends.

Emarginate: with a shallow notch in the apical margin.

Endemic: confined to a certain, usually rather restricted area, and not found elsewhere.

Epiphyte: a plant that grows on another plant, but is not nourished by it (hence, not parasitic); an air-plant.

Epiphytic: pertaining to epiphyte.

Equitant: folded and standing inside each other, in two ranks, in the manner of the leaves of an iris.

Exotic: not native, foreign.

Fimbriate: fringed.

Genera: plural of genus.

Generic: of or pertaining to a genus.

Genus: a subdivision of a family, consisting of one or more species which show similar characteristics and appear to have a common ancestry.

Glabrous: smooth; devoid of hair or pubescence.

Glaucous: covered with a bluish gray, bluish green, or whitish bloom that will not rub off.

Gynostemium: see Column.

Hapuu: Hawaiian term for tree-fern fiber.

Herbaceous: herblike; not woody.

Herbarium: a collection of dried (or otherwise preserved) plant specimens, annotated and identified.

Hermaphrodite: a flower having the organs, characteristics, or attributes of both sexes, hence, perfect; a flower that bears both stamens and pistils; a bisexual flower.

Hermaphroditic: pertaining to hermaphrodite.

Host: In a biological sense, signifying any plant or animal affording lodgment or subsistence to a parasitic or commensal organism. This term is used with relative incorrectness in reference to epiphytic orchids, although it is often found in the literature.

Imbricate: overlapping, like shingles on a roof.

Incised: with the margins cut into sharp, deep, irregular teeth.

Inclining: bent down from the horizontal.

Indigenous: native; not introduced; not exotic.

Inflorescence: the general arrangement and disposition of the flowers on an axis; mode of flower-bearing; much more frequently used (and technically less correctly) in the sense of a flower-cluster.

Internode: portion of a stem situated between the nodes, or joints.

Keel: a projecting ridge on a surface, basically rather similar to the keel of a boat.

Keeled: provided with a keel.

Keiki: Hawaiian term, widely used by orchidists throughout the world to signify an offshoot or offset from a plant.

Labellum: lip, particularly that of an orchid flower.

Lamella: a thin flat plate or scale. Plural—*lamellae.*

Lamina: the blade or expanded part of a leaf, petal, or other structure.

Lanceolate: lance-shaped; several times longer than broad and tapering from near the base to the pointed apex.

Lateral: of or pertaining to the side of an organism or its parts.

Ligulate: strap-shaped.

Limb: the broad expanded part of a clawed segment of a flower.

Linear: narrow and comparitively long, with parallel margins.

Lip: In orchids, the third petal of the corolla series, which has been so adapted as to appear a distinct segment; labellum is a synonym.

Lithophyte: a plant that inhabits rocks.

Lithophytic: pertaining to lithophyte.

Lobate: furnished with lobes.

Lobulate: furnished with lobules.

Lobule: a small lobe.

Malquique: Mexican term for tree-fern, and also for tree-fern fiber.

Marginate: with a distinct border or margin.

Membranaceous: thin and more or less translucent.

Monopodial: growing only from the apex of the plant (from its terminal bud); characteristic of all orchids of the subtribe *Sarcanthinae.*

Morphology: the science that treats of forms or of the transformation of organs or parts.

Multigeneric: of many genera; usually used in reference to hybrids combining several genera.

Node: a joint or knot; in orchids applied particularly to the joints of stems or pseudobulbs.

Nomenclature: system of naming.

Obcordate: inversely cordate; heart-shaped with the attachment at the apex.

Oblique: with unequal sides; asymmetrical.

Oblong: two to four times as long as broad, the sides being almost parallel.

Obtuse: blunt at the tip.

Orbicular: spherical.

Orbiculate: circular.

Orchidist: one who collects or is interested in orchids horticulturally.

Orchidologist: a botanist who specializes in the study of orchids.

Orchidology: the particular branch of botany dealing with the study of orchids.

Oval: broadly elliptical and slightly contracted upward.

Ovate: egg-shaped, with the broader end downward.

Ovary: the part of the pistil (female portion) of a flower in which the ovules or rudimentary seeds are borne; in orchids the ovary is combined with the pedicel to form the pedicellate ovary.

Ovoid: egg-shaped, the larger end toward the stem or axis; used in a three-dimensional sense as opposed to ovate.

Panicle: a compound raceme; a compound, more or less open inflorescence in which the lower branches are longer and blossom earlier than the upper ones.

Paniculate: arranged in a panicle.

Parasite: an organism that derives its sustenance from another plant, called the *host;* no orchids are true parasites.

Parthenogenesis: development of seed without fertilization or fecundation, but by stimulus only.

Pedicel: the stalk of an individual flower in an inflorescence which is comprised of more than one flower.

Pedicellate: borne on a pedicel; also by extension resembling a pedicel; in orchids, the combined pedicel and ovary give rise to the term pedicellate ovary.

Peduncle: stalk of a flower-cluster or of a flower.

Perfect: with both staminate and pistillate parts in the same flower.

Perianth: floral envelope, consisting of the calyx and corolla; the perianth of an orchid flower consists of the sepals, petals, and lip.

Petal: one of the separate segments of the corolla of a flower, usually colored other than green, making up the inner and upper series of a floral envelope or flower; in orchids, one of the petals is normally modified into a lip, or labellum.

Petiole: the stalk by which a leaf is attached to a stem.

Phylogenetical: pertaining to the race history of a type or group of organisms; the evolutional system of a type or group of organisms.

Pistil: the female or seed-producing organ of a flower, consisting usually of ovary, style, and stigma. In orchids the pistil is referred to as the column or gynostemium.

Plicate: folded like a fan.

Pollinium: in orchids, a coherent mass of pollen found in the anthers. Plural—*pollinia.*

Polymorphic: occurring in several distinct forms.

Protocorm: in orchids, the initial minute cormlike plantlet produced immediately after germination, prior to the production of any leaves, roots, etc.

Pseudobulb: thickened or bulblike stems of certain orchids, borne above the ground or substratum.

Quadrigeneric: pertaining to four genera; used particularly in reference to hybrids combining members of four genera.

Raceme: a simple, elongated cluster with stalked flowers.

Racemose: growing in the form of a raceme.

Rachis: the axis of a spike, raceme, or branch of a panicle.

Resupinate: upside down; turned over; inverted in position by a twist of the axis or, in orchids, of the pedicellate ovary.

Retuse: with the apex rounded or obtuse and shallowly notched.

Revolute: rolled backward from the margin upon the lower surface.

Rhizome: a rootstock that is actually a stem or branch, but that grows beneath the surface of the ground or creeps along the substratum, and gives rise to the plant's main stem.

Rosette: a dense basal cluster of leaves.

Rupicolous: dwelling in or on rocks or stones.

Saprophyte: an organism that lives on dead organic matter.

Saprophytic: pertaining to a saprophyte.

Sarcanthad: a member of the orchid subtribe *Sarcanthinae.*

Secund: borne on one side only; unilateral.

Segment: one of the parts of a leaf, petal, sepal, or perianth that is divided but not truly compound; also used as a synonym for any part of a floral envelope.

Semiepiphytic: partly or somewhat epiphytic; applied to certain plants that are found growing in pockets of humus which has collected in the crotches of tree branches, hence which are not truly epiphytic but only appear so.

Sepal: one of the segments forming the outer and lower series of a floral envelope or flower.

Sepaline: pertaining to the sepals.

Serrate: saw-toothed marginally, with the teeth pointing toward the apex.

Sessile: without a stem or stalk; stalkless.

Sheath: any long, more or less tubular structure surrounding an organ or part.

Spatulate: shaped like a spoon or spatula.

Species: a group of plants (or animals) showing integradation among its individuals or races, and one or more characteristics in common which definitely separate it from any other group.

Specific: pertaining to a species; definite.

Spreading: standing outward or horizontally.

Spur: a hollow tubular or saclike extension of a floral organ, as of a sepal or petal; it usually contains nectar-secreting glands within it.

Staminate: male; bearing stamens only.

Staminode: a sterile or abortive stamen, or a structure resembling such and borne in the staminal part of a flower; staminodes occur in the flowers of the orchid subtribe *Cypripedilinae.* Synonym—*staminodium.*

Stellate: resembling a star.

Stigma: the portion of the pistil of a flower which receives the pollen for fertilization of the ovules; in orchids it is a sticky cavity or excavation, usually situated on the under-surface of the upper part of the column.

Striate: striped; marked with longitudinal lines, grooves, or ridges.

Style: the stalklike portion of a pistil which connects the stigma with the ovary; in orchids this term is seldom utilized.

Succulent: juicy or fleshy.

Sulcate: grooved, especially with deep longitudinal furrows.

Symbiosis: the condition of two distinct organisms growing together in harmony for mutual advantage, as the relationship of the specialized symbiotic fungi found in orchids which assist in the germination of orchid seed in the wild.

Symbiotic: adjective used in reference to the condition of symbiosis.

Sympodial: continuing to grow by successive lateral shoots, instead of by the terminal bud; the opposite of monopodial.

Taxonomy: the science of classification, dealing with the arrangement of plants (or animals) into groups according to natural relationships.

Terete: circular in transverse section.

Terminal: apical; produced at the end.

Terrestrial: of the earth; growing in soil.

Throat: the lower part of the tube of orchids having a tubular lip.

Trigeneric: of three genera; usually used in reference to hybrids combining members of three genera.

Trilobate: with three lobes.

Truncate: square at the apex, as if cut off.

Undulate: wavy; with wavy margins.

Unisexual: with flowers of one sex only, either staminate (male) or pistillate (female).

Venose: veined; full of veins.

Viscid: sticky; glutinous.

Wing: any more or less thin expansion from a surface, typically at a decided angle to the surface.

Xaxim: Brazilian term for tree-fern and also for the fiber thereof.

Zygomorphic: capable of being divided into two symmetrical halves only by a single longitudinal plane passing through the axis; all orchid flowers are zygomorphic.

Index

INDEX

Bold face numerals indicate an illustration.

284   INDEX

saprophyte, 9
sarcanthad, 240
Sarcanthinae, 15, 179, 271, 272
Sarcanthus, 272
  paniculatus, **34**
Sarcochileae, 271, 272
Sarcochilus, 16, 271
Sarcoglottis, 266
Sarcorhynchus, 273
Sarcostoma, 268
Sarcothera, 245
Satyridium, 264
Satyriinae, 264
Satyrium, 7, 264
Saundersia, 271
Saundersiinae, 271
Sauroglossum, 266
Scaphosepalum, 267
Scaphyglottis, 16, 214, 268
  Behrii, 214
  violacea, **215**
Scelochilus, 270
Schizochilus, 264
Schizodium, 264
Schlechter, Rudolph, 263
Schlimia, 270
Schoenorchis, 272
Schombocattleya, 245, 249
Schombodiacrium, 245, 249
Schomboepidendrum, 245
Schombolaelia, 245, 249
Schomburgkia, 95, 172, 243, 249
  tibicinis, 95, 173
  undulata, 95, **174**
Schwartzkopffia, 264
"Scorpion Orchids," 108
screw pines, 60
Scuticaria, 214, 270
  Hadweni, 215, 216
  Steelii, **216**
seed capsule, 74, **75** 254
seed, sowing of, 74, 76
seed, structure of, 76
seedlings, **82**
Selenipedium, 202, 253, 263
Semiphajus, 269
semiterrestrial, **52**
sepaline tube, 27
Sepalosaccus, 270
Sepalosiphon, 268
sepals, **22**, 26, 27
Serapias, 263
Sievekingia, 270
Sigmatostalix, 271
Silvorchis, 264
slat-house, 43, **44**, 45
Smithorchis, 264

Sobennikoffia, 272
Sobralia, 7, 17, 23, 187, 216, 265
  decora, 217
  leucoxantha, **217**
  macrantha, 7, 217
Sobraliinae, 265
Sodiroella, 271
Solenangis, 273
Solenidium, 271
Solenocentrum, 266
Sophrocattleya, 245
Sophrolaelia, 245
Sophrolaeliocattleya, 245
Sophronitella, 268
Sophronitis, 173, 218, 268
  cernua, 95
  coccinea, 95, **218**
  grandiflora, 218
Spathoglottis, 62, 95, 218, 269
  aurea, 219
  hybrids, 95
  plicata, 95, 219, **220**
Spathophaius, 245
species, 259
Sphagnum, 47
sphagnum moss, 46, 47
Sphyrarhynchus, 273
Sphyrastylis, 271
Spiculaea, 265
"Spider Orchids," 117
Spiranthes, 266
Spiranthinae, 266
spur, 28
staminode, **21**, 24, 253
staminodium, **21**, 24, 253
Stanhopea, 16, 28, 51, 99, 136, 137, 163, 219, 270
  graveolens, 95, 220
  Wardii, 95, **221**
Stelis, 7, 23, 221, 266
  ciliaris, **222**
Stellilabium, 271
stems, 20
Stenia, 270
Stenocoryne, 270
Stenoglossum, 267
Stenoglottis, 264
  longifolia, 95
Stenoptera, 266
Stereosandra, 266
Steveniella, 264
Stevenorchis, 264
stigma, 23, **24**, 253
stigmatic surface, 23
Stigmatodactylus, 265
Stolzia, 268
Stolziinae, 268